Blue Jolts

True Stories from the Cuckoo's Nest

BLUE JOLTS

Compiled by
Charles Steir

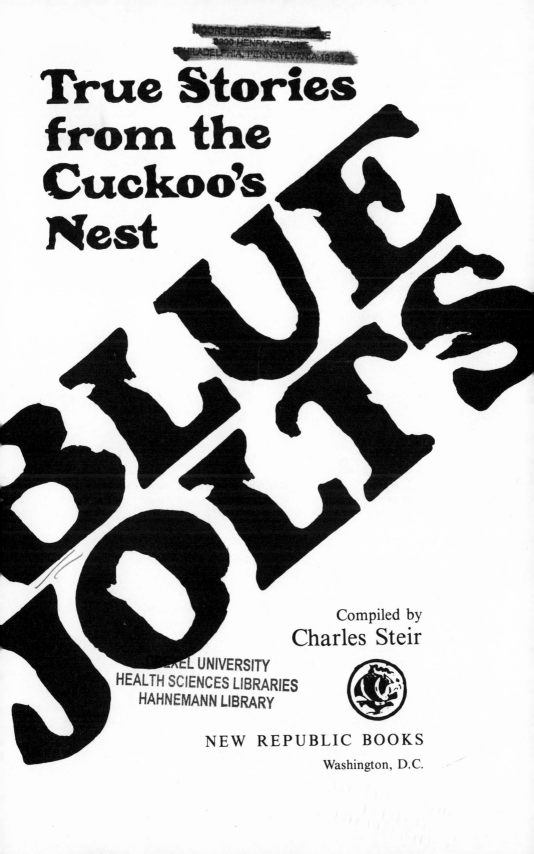

NEW REPUBLIC BOOKS

Washington, D.C.

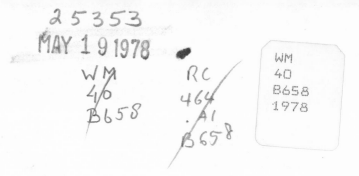

Published in 1978 by
New Republic Books
1220 Nineteenth St., N.W.
Washington, D.C. 20036

Library of Congress Cataloging in Publication Data
Main entry under title:

Blue jolts.

  Bibliography: p.
  Includes index.
  1. Psychiatric hospital care—Biography. 2. Mental illness—Biography. I. Steir,
Charles, 1947-
RC464.A1B58   362.2'1'0922 [B]   77-21412
ISBN 0-915220-30-X

Trade distribution by Simon and Schuster
A Division of Gulf & Western Corporation
New York, New York 10020
Order No. 0-671-22969-9

New Republic Books wishes to thank the following copyright holders for their
permission to use the following articles and excerpts:

"Kicking, Screaming and Cursing" and "Passing the Buck" by Louise Wilson,
reprinted by permission of G.P. Putnam's Sons and Harold Ober Associates,
Incorporated, from *This Stranger, My Son* by Louise Wilson. Copyright © 1968 by
Louise Wilson.

"Conspiracy Against the Weak" by David Viscott, reprinted by permission of Arbor
House Publishing Company, Inc. Copyright © 1972 by David S. Viscott.

Printed in the United States of America

To Dr. Thomas Szasz

Table of Contents

Preface   xvii

I. ADMISSION

Introduction   3

1. "KICKING, SCREAMING AND
   CURSING"   Louise Wilson   10
The parents of a fourteen-year-old boy force him into a mental hospital.

2. "CONSPIRACY AGAINST THE
   WEAK"   David Viscott   17
A doctor fights an unnecessary admission.

3. "WHERE THEY CAN FORCE
   PEOPLE TO STAY"   Dakin Williams   23
An intern needles Tennessee Williams from behind to keep him at the hospital.

4. "THE KIDNAPPING"   Earl Long   25
Governor Earl Long of Louisiana tells how he was taken to a mental hospital in Texas and then committed to a public mental hospital in his home state.

5. "WHAT'S THE VERDICT?"   Janet Gotkin   27
Mother and father numbly assent to daughter's hospitalization.

6. "THE LETDOWN"   Sarah E. Lorenz   30
Parents do not expect the reception they get on a psychiatric ward.

7. "STAFF HAS SPOKEN!"   Walter Fisher et al. 38
An incestuous couple is institutionalized.

8. "ADMISSION STRUGGLE"   A.E. Hotchner   39
Ernest Hemingway tries to kill himself three times as friends take him to a mental hospital.

9. "THE INSANITY BIT" (I)   Seymour Krim   43
Krim illustrates the containment function of mental hospitals.

10. "A SORTING PROBLEM"   Sergeant Albert Sykora   51
A police officer discusses his problems in hospitalizing people.

xi

11. "THE START OF THE WAY
   OF THE CROSS"   Valery Tarsis   53
Soviet dissident Tarsis is hauled off to a mental institution.

12. "KAVKA AND POUND"   Charles Olson   56
*Hospitalized Ezra Pound chafes Jews on medical grounds, and is himself
dissected psychiatrically by his doctor, Kavka, and by visitor Olson.*

13. "A NEED TO DISRUPT THE
   LIVES OF OTHERS"   Robert Coles   61
A southern judge sends a black civil rights worker to a mental hospital.

14. "FORCE AND FRAUD"   Jeffrey R. Solomon   64
Admission procedures so agitate a woman that her depression subsides.

15. "TOO MENTALLY ILL"   Lawrence Al Siebert   69
*A Menninger psychologist complains about deceit in the commitment
process.*

16. "ADVANTAGE OF FORCE"   Antonin Artaud   71
Artaud reproaches hospital doctors for their lack of empathy.

II. TREATMENT

Introduction   77

17. "ANGER, LONELINESS,
   DETACHMENT, AND BOREDOM"   William A. Weitz   84
A psychologist-pseudopatient learns why inmates react as they do.

18. "ALLEVIATING SCHIZOPHRENIC
   THINKING"   Lloyd Cotter   88
*An American psychiatrist at a mental hospital in Vietnam shocks and
starves the inmates into working.*

19. "IDEOLOGICAL TREATMENT"   Leonid Plyushch   91
Soviet psychiatrists try to erase a dissenter's beliefs.

20. "WORRY WARTS"   Ivan Belknap   98
*Sociologist Belknap observes how shock is used to control uncoopera-
tive inmates.*

21. "SIXTY COMAS"   R. Frederick West 101
A preacher gets insulin shock.

22. "MIRACLE CURE"   Paul Warr 104
A bumbling psychiatrist tries one therapeutic scheme after another.

23. "WONDER DRUGS"   Louise Bogan 109
Bogan wryly describes the effects of drugging.

24. "THE WRONG LESSON"   Alma Stone 112
A psychiatric social worker watches while an attendant beats an inmate.

25. "THE FRENCH KISS AND
   THE PINCH"   Robbie Skeist 115
Head nurse becomes upset when an orderly lets a male inmate kiss him.

xii

26. "HOSPRISON"   Jan Marks 117
Doctor-inmate Marks shows how attendants exert control.

27. "MUTUAL FURY"   David Clark 121
Staff members accuse each other of not maintaining heat on the wards.

28. "CONDEMNED DREAMS"   Carl Solomon 123
Beat poet Solomon describes a Halloween masquerade ball.

29. "I DON'T BELIEVE IN
    MENTAL TORTURE"   Milton Rokeach 125
A psychologist reinforces the delusions of an inmate who believes himself Christ.

30. "STUPID GIRL. STUPID GIRL.
    SCRUB. SCRUB. SCRUB."   D.L. Stannard 127
An inmate has to scrub a bathroom floor with a toothbrush.

31. "VEGETABLES DON'T CRY"   Eileen Walkenstein 130
A doctor describes a ghoulish lobotomy.

32. "PATIENT GOVERNMENT"   Jane Fry 134
An inmate grievance committee futilely debates a minor problem.

33. "BACK WARD"   Marshall Edelson 136
A psychiatric resident rouses half the most disturbed male ward by making a simple request.

34. "SCHIZOPHRENIA CHRONIC
    UNDIFFERENTIATED TYPE"   Jackie Daymoon 138
An attendant who tries to restore an old inmate's interest in life is rebuked.

35. "VERTICAL EXTRACTION"   David Vail 140
An inmate can't make even the simplest choices after long confinement.

36. "REBIRTH IN A THERAPEUTIC
    COMMUNITY"   Lewis Killian 142
A sociology professor praises his hospital experience.

37. "MOTHER-SON SYMBIOSIS"   Sarah E. Lorenz 158
Joint hospital treatment drives a mother to despair over her son.

III. RELEASE

Introduction   165

38. "PASSING THE BUCK"   Louise Wilson 170
Staff recommends that a young inmate move on to an adult hospital.

39. "TURNING THE TABLES"   United Press 176
An inmate releases himself by admitting a staff psychiatrist to another hospital.

40. "THREATENED WITH JAIL"   Jacquelyn E. Murray 178
Nursing instructor Murray sees staff threaten and pressure recalcitrant inmates and relatives.

41. "THE LITTLE TRICKS"   Judith Kruger 180
An inmate tries to satisfy a discharge panel.

42. "ARE YOU HAPPY HERE?"   Paul Warr 185
A doctor snares a hapless inmate with a loaded question.

43. "SHE'S OBVIOUSLY PARANOID"   Robert Perrucci 191
Staff manages to "elicit pathological content" from an inmate.

44. "RELIGIOUS PROPAGANDA"   Gennady M. Shimanov 195
A Soviet psychiatric board looks for illness in a religious citizen.

45. "THE HEAD BOY"   Donald Johnson 200
A doctor-lawyer inmate connives a quick release.

46. "SPILLED SUGAR"   Anna Mary Wells 204
*A released English professor finds that her colleagues expect her to act
like a "mental patient."*

47. "TOO SICK FOR
      THIS KIND OF WORK"   George S. Glass 209
*Three attendants who have been hospitalized on their own service are
rejected by their fellow workers.*

48. "IMBALANCED"   Eloise Davenport 211
Medical specialists take an "ex-patient's" physical complaints lightly.

49. "THE INSANITY BIT" (II)   Seymour Krim 217
Krim's literary friends adhere to the old conceptions of insanity.

50. "INSTITUTIONALISM"   John Neary 223
A long-term inmate has trouble adjusting to life on the outside.

51. "COUNTING THE MAD"   227

Notes   229

References and Supplementary Bibliography   231

Index   241

Doctor Gordon was fitting two metal plates on either side of my head. He buckled them into place with a strap that dented my forehead, and gave me a wire to bite.

I shut my eyes.

There was a brief silence, like an indrawn breath.

Then something bent down and took hold of me and shook me like the end of the world. Whee-ee-ee-ee-ee, it shrilled, through an air crackling with blue light, and with each flash a great jolt drubbed me till I thought my bones would break and the sap fly out of me like a split plant.

I wondered what terrible thing it was that I had done.

Sylvia Plath
The Bell Jar

Preface

In this book mental patients tell about mental hospitals. Famous and powerful people as well as ordinary individuals show how vulnerable they were to hospitalization. As they speak up, their experiences and pain become real to us. We understand how it feels to be admitted, "treated," and released, and to be permanently labeled a mental patient. The immediacy and power of these first-hand accounts, interspersed with contributions by hospital workers, give a better understanding of the patient's predicament than any number of case reports.

Virtually all the events described in this book take place since the end of 1953, when the number of people in mental hospitals was peaking toward an astounding 700,000 in the United States and 140,000 in England. By the beginning of 1978 the number of patients on any given day will have decreased sharply to about 200,000 in the United States and about 80,000 in England. But these figures are deceptive. While the number of long-term inmates has been greatly reduced, more and more people have been entering mental hospitals and wards for shorter and shorter stays. This large-scale transformation of people into mental patients and "ex-mental patients" makes the issue of mental hospitalization more current than ever.

The date that appears at the end of each selection is the actual date of each episode, not the publication date. All notes and references appear at the end of the book.

I

Admission

Introduction

They said I was mad; and I said they were
mad, and, damn them, they outvoted me.

Nathaniel Lee, in Max Byrd
Visits to Bedlam

Sanity a trick of agreement.

Allen Ginsberg
Kaddish

The persons hitherto reckoned as mad, you
see, became normal last night at eleven,
accordant with Reason in its newest phase.
And more, if the matter be rightly regarded,
it's patent that, at the aforementioned hour,
the sane folks, so called, began forthwith to
rave.

Henrik Ibsen
Peer Gynt

Mental patients are rejects from home, school, work, and society at large. Their behavior is inappropriate or inconvenient and occasionally dangerous. When others find them intolerable, their isolation makes them less able to resist hospitalization, especially if they are poor, members of an ethnic minority, physically disabled, old, or young. Louise Wilson's description of the forced admission of her problem son, "Kicking, Screaming, and Cursing," and Dr. Viscott's chronicle of the hospitalization of a normal teenage boy following a family dispute, "Conspiracy against the Weak," demonstrate the vulnerability of the young. But even the

3

powerful are subject to hospitalization: Tennessee Williams and Governor Earl Long of Louisiana were both hospitalized against their will. Their experiences are described by Tennessee's brother Dakin in "Where They Can Force People to Stay," and by Long himself in "The Kidnapping." The very process of hospitalization, often enacted in ritual rites of passage as in Janet Gotkin's "What's the Verdict?" transforms people from disturbing to disturbed, deprived to depraved, defiant to deviant, insufferable to suffering, in sum, from people to patients. Once admitted into the hospital, they may be turned into research objects, as in Sarah Lorenz's "The Letdown."

Hospitalization shields the community from a person in the guise of protecting him from himself: "Surely it is better that silly claptrap or obscenities or outbursts against the people whom normally a patient loves the most be poured out before doctors and nurses than before neighbors," concludes mental hygienist Edith Stern.[1] According to psychologist Kent Miller, "Mental health agencies are increasingly charged with the responsibility of dealing with irritating, troublesome people in the community—reflecting a conflict that has existed over time but has not been clearly recognized."[2] Former state mental hospital superintendent William Sheeley admits that many inmates simply are not emotionally disturbed: "For years the community has sent us people with little or no mental illness, but with limited ability to compete in the world . . . unreconstructible Peter Pans . . . old people . . . and naughty folk."[3] Psychologist Walter Fisher's account ("Staff Has Spoken!") of the way a mental hospital disposes of a couple who ignore community norms supports Sheeley's viewpoint.

Surely it is a violation of civil liberties to force people into treatment who are merely eccentric or dangerous only to *themselves.* Unconscious people and people too gravely disabled to function or to seek aid can and should be treated as medical emergencies in general hospitals, unless and until they protest that they do not want help.[4] Individuals less severely disabled yet unable to care for themselves, and incompetents, may be placed under guardianship after judicial review, but they needn't be hospitalized in a mental institution. After all, forced treatment can reinforce the very helplessness it is meant to avoid. Mental hospital administrator Willard Larson finds that psychiatrists in particular are ". . . seriously underestimating the degree of responsibility that psychiatric patients will assume, and in misjudging this, grievously decimate the new patient's wavering self-esteem and self-image as a competent, self-sufficient individual, albeit a man in a crisis, and thus cause to come true in the worst, negative sense of the 'self-fulfilling prophesy,' the physician's fears of a dependent, irresponsible, ineffectual, and unpredictable human being possibly, if not probably, crippled for life."[5]

Given the extreme case of the suicidal person, the wise course seems to be to offer assistance in overcoming the crisis, but not to enforce hospital dependency. If a person is determined to kill himself, he can do so after, if not during his hospitalization, even with the most understanding and intensive care. Ernest Hemingway, whose hospitalization A. E. Hotchner describes in "Admission Struggle," committed suicide in spite of coerced treatment.

Some people who are dangerous to themselves are also unintentionally dangerous to others, for example, people who persistently forget to shut off their cooking. Such people can be restrained by informal warnings or by civil proceedings that compel them to find new lodgings, with nursing care if necessary. Similarly, heads of households who harm family members by precipitously impoverishing themselves can be placed under guardianship; children are under the automatic guardianship of their parents. Civil remedies protect the community reasonably well without entailing involuntary hospitalization. A cautious approach is called for in these instances, particularly since dangerousness is often exaggerated or even entirely concocted. For instance, a San Francisco geriatric screening team making ". . . home visits discovered in practically every instance. . . . family feuds, neighborhood feuds, one relative wanting to get rid of another elderly relative by stating the person was dangerous and so on. . . ."[6]

People have learned that commitment requires evidence of dangerousness; when they want to commit someone, they frequently invent plausible grounds:

In one case, persons representing themselves as spokesmen for an ethnically oriented social and political action group accompanied a patient to the admitting room of the hospital to assure her admission to a locked ward; they contended that she had thrown her newborn infant into a trash can on the street. Because of the nature of her behavior, and the social pressure, the patient was accepted for direct admission to the ICU [intensive care unit,

Bronx Psychiatric Center]. We later learned that the story was pure fabrication. The community had defined the patient as a nuisance, and it wanted to make sure that she stayed in the hospital.[7]

Compounding the tendency toward labeling admittees dangerous, "psychiatrists ignore the statutory requirement that involuntary patients must be dangerous as well as mentally ill, and simply commit anyone they feel needs treatment."[8] Their evasiveness is understandable, since it is very difficult to predict dangerousness in people who have not violated the law,[9] and hospitalization of such people would constitute preventive detention. Further, there is exceedingly little crime among released inmates without previous criminal records.[10] All these circumstances suggest the need for judicial safeguards.

What should be done about the deliberately and criminally dangerous, as well as the "chomosomally deficient" and other "unintentional" offenders who try to derive benefit from their crimes, and individuals who have fits of "insane" temper? The community has a right to protect itself from those whose violent or threatening behavior constitutes a clear danger. Isn't society best protected when arsonists are not psychiatrically labeled "pyromaniac," but are made responsible for their acts in the criminal justice system, with its procedural protections and due process? Psychologist Al Siebert persuasively argues, "Calling someone 'sick' because of how he acts merely excuses us from responsibility for what we do to him. It would be more honest to say, 'We're locking you up because we don't like what you're doing.' We can and should take action against someone who has lost control of himself and is intruding into the lives and minds of others."[11]

Honesty should replace the hypocrisy of the advice given in a popular guide for attendants: "The idea that a patient is ill is a far better reason to give him for his detention than that he is too troublesome, dangerous, or foolish to be abroad."[12] Seymour Krim perceptively enlarges on this theme in "The Insanity Bit, (I)." All too common is the position of sociologist Don Martindale, who, together with psychiatric social worker Edith Martindale, suggest that ". . . in all transitional situations borderline between mental illness and outright criminality, the most humane response is almost always to opt for involuntary hospitalization for treatment, rather than to send the individual to prison. This permits the offender to disassociate himself from his antisocial behavior by attributing it to his illness."[13]

Sociologist Thomas Scheff points out the negative results of the sickness approach: "When a residual rule-breaker organizes his behavior within the framework of mental disorder, and when his organization is validated by others, particularly prestigeful others such as physicians, he is 'hooked' and will proceed on a career of chronic deviance."[14] Further, ". . . hospitalization confirms for the patient the idea that he is out of control," according to analyst John Schimel.[15] In "A Sorting Problem," it is Police Sergeant Sykora who asks the key question about hospitalizing people: "Is a law being broken?" The law certainly allows a decided leeway for the just prosecution of menaces and extreme nuisances, while studies indicate that inmates and former inmates are less dangerous than people in the population at large."[16] With its safeguards, the criminal approach to disruptive behavior would probably lead to only a modest possible increase in jailing and imprisonment, but to much less hospitalization, since people not convicted of a crime would not be hospitalized.

After extensive study a legislative health committee in California concluded: "What is required is a voluntary system for providing prompt and appropriate assistance to citizens suffering from mental disorders without any loss of liberty; and an involuntary system for identifying and separating dangerous persons from the community, with full due process of law, and providing them with such treatment and custody as may be required."[17] Such arrangements are far from being accomplished. Mental hospitals historically have served, and now serve in large part, as short-stay jailhouses for noncriminals. As early as 1839 an anonymous writer recognized that "the inmates of an . . . asylum are in point of fact in a prison."[18] Mental hospital psychiatrist Maurice Grimes refers to ". . . state hospitals and other prisons."[19] Thomas Szasz strongly maintains that ". . . the institutional psychiatrist is a jailer."[20]

Some social scientists go so far as to contend, "The situation of the hospital inmate is certainly less extreme than that of his counterpart in a concentration camp, but the difference is neither qualitative nor decisive."[21] Ironically, a psychiatric nursing text defines an inmate's comparison of the two types of "total institutions" (sociologist Erving Goffman's concept[22]), as disorientation and as being "unaware of the correct date, time, place, etc. For example, 'This isn't a hospital. It's a concentration camp!'"[23] With noteworthy similarity, a Soviet psychiatric board found that dissenter Vladimir Borisov displayed "an inability in orientation and an incorrect understanding of his surroundings. For instance, he took the hospital for a concentration camp, the doctors for sadists. . . ."[24]

The Soviet use of mental hospitals for political repression illustrates the larger theme that people in conflict, people who don't like or can't control each other, turn to the mental hospital. The practice has been widespread. The Nazis, for instance, sent political opponents to mental hospitals,[25] and eventually murdered 275,000 inmates.[26] The Chinese communists have brainwashing centers called "hospitals for ideological reform."[27] The modern Soviets stymie political dissenters by railroading them into mental hospitals, to be "sorted out" as in the case of Valery Tarsis in "The Start of the Way of the Cross." In the United States, Ezra Pound was hospitalized instead of being tried for treason. Charles Olson describes a visit to the poet in "Kavka and Pound." Also in the United States, officials have identified intergrationists as the "lunatic fringe" by sending them to mental hospitals. In the selection by Dr. Coles, "A Need to Disrupt the Lives of Others," a hospital psychiatrist tries to convince a young black civil rights worker that his activities are part of a personal pathology.

Contrary to reality, every inmate is told that he is a sick patient who needs medical healing: ". . . based on force and fraud, and justified by 'medical necessity,' the prime purpose of [institutional] psychiatric treatments—whether utilizing drugs, electricity, surgery, or confinement, especially if imposed on unconsenting clients—is to authenticate the subject as a 'patient,' the psychiatrist as a 'doctor,' and the intervention as a form of 'treatment.'"[28] Witness the deceit abetted by police coercion in the admission of a depressed woman in Jeffrey Solomon's "Force and Fraud," and staff subversion of commitment hearings in Al Siebert's "Too Mentally Ill." Institutional psychiatrists will even resort to inventing guardianship requirements to ensure admission or frustrate release: "If it is a relative who refuses to sign a petition, he is told that he must sign a statement of release and assume responsibility for the patient, although legally there is no such requirement. When faced with this instruction, very often the relative will reconsider and sign the petition."[29]

Mental hospital fraud is pervasive and apparently universal. A British psychologist-inmate reports that "On admission, patients may be asked to sign an agreement with the director of the hospital that they will agree to remain in the hospital for a minimum specified period of time. Such agreements are not legally binding, but many patients presumably do not appreciate this."[30] Senior staff members at Bronx Psychiatric Center offer this vignette: "A young male patient arrived with several notes scrawled on the admitting papers sent from the community general hospital indicating that he was 'to be admitted to a closed ward by order of Commissioner "X," New York City Department of Health.' While we were under no obligation to heed these instructions, we did so. Within a day it was learned that no such commissioner existed."[31] Antonin Artaud puts the matter well when he reproaches mental hospital doctors for having ". . . only one advantage, namely force" over the inmates.

Is the force and fraud justified? Certainly not for the small number of inmates who are admitted because of medical-neurological problems.[32] They could be diagnosed and treated voluntarily in *real* hospitals and clinics. For the majority of inmates who simply have problems in living that make them intolerable to others and sometimes to themselves, medical quarantine is unfairly and illogically applied to a nebulous, contrived "mental illness" (examined by Dr. Thomas Szasz in *The Manufacture of Madness*[33]). People in distress must be offered voluntary care only. Compulsory institutionalization should not force anyone innocent of crime into the official status of deviant.

"Kicking, Screaming and Cursing"

LOUISE WILSON

Fourteen-year-old Tony wore dirty clothes, gobbled his food, fought with his brothers and sisters, cursed, and disobeyed his parents—though he got along with the maid, Hanna. He punched his brother in the nose when mocked with, "Tony goes to the psychiatrist! Tony goes to the psychiatrist!" Tony had in fact been sent to a number of psychiatrists—he had already quit the last, Dr. Collins—who saw varying degrees of "illness" in the boy.

Is Tony merely a rebellious, disruptive boy, or is he "paranoid schizophrenic," as he is eventually labeled? His mother takes pains to characterize his babyhood and childhood as hectic and troubled and emphasizes his early differentness and intractability. She also writes that while he was at home, he thought his food was being poisoned, but makes no connection with the fact that she and her husband, Jack, had secretly put tranquilizers into his milk.

They finally find a mental hospital for juveniles that pleases them, "The School," and force Tony in. He stays at The School for three years, but the hopeful "straightening out," to use the mother's expression, does not take place. See the excerpt in the Release section for the outcome.

I HAD never known that the great metropolitan dailes are filled with advertisements for special schools. Of course, they all sound equally attractive and competent. I began to pore over them. I called several on the telephone and had to rule out the first few because they would not even consider taking a child who would not come willingly. But that was at the core of our problem: Tony was absolutely unwilling to leave home.

We visited several of the schools and were very discouraged. To begin with, the physical environments were shocking. Some of these places were so poor and barren they would make a normal person feel depressed.

I remember one which sounded most promising when I talked to the director on the telephone. He was a well-spoken man with a doctorate and was a specialist in the psychology of the emotionally disturbed adolescent. His school occupied a piece of acreage carved out of second-growth woods and sumac scrub on a main highway. He and his wife lived in a small frame house, and about fifty feet away were the students' quarters, in a long frame building shaped like a railway car. It was divided into cubicles much like a boarding kennel, clean, well-heated and bare.

Outside there was a basketball net nailed to a tree and a very small pond "where they can skate when it freezes over," we were told.

"What else is there for recreation?" we asked.

"Oh, we take nature walks, we drive into town."

The town through which we passed consisted of four or five blocks of stores and a shabby movie theater. I couldn't imagine what the boys could do after they got there.

"We have a psychiatrist who comes over on Thursdays," the director said. "And of course the curriculum is college preparatory. I teach and I have a well-qualified assistant. We have some very fine students here."

"And the fee?" Jack inquired. He was merely filling the silence, because I knew he would have never left Tony here. I wondered what kind of parents possibly could have done so.

"Five hundred dollars a month," was the reply. "All inclusive."

Jack said we would think it over and have Tony's doctor get in touch with him.

"I do want to add one thing," the man said. "Whether or not you decide to send your son to my school, I must advise you to send him somewhere. Don't try to keep him at home."

He was really decent; undoubtedly, given funds, he could have set up something much better. He was surely aware of how disgracefully inadequate his facilities were. But it only showed how desperate the need is and that people in desperate need settle for almost anything.

"You can see for yourselves that your boy isn't improving at home.

11

If anything, he is getting worse, as the family's endurance wears thin."

"That's true."

"And it is simply not fair to the other children. Take the boy away before irreparable damage is done. That's my most candid advice to you."

We thanked him and drove away. His admonitions made a great deal more sense to me than what I had been hearing from Dr. Collins about endurance.

Or did it only make more sense because it offered me an easy way out, because it was what I wanted to be told?

Now events picked up momentum. What had been a very gradual descent, with interludes of apparently slight improvement, now suddenly became that steep-pitched slide. The gentle springtime was ominous. There was no Dr. Collins to run to via the telephone in emergencies. So often his advice had been useless or impossible to carry out; still it had been something, a willing ear, an encouraging word. Now Jack and I alone, or rather Hanna and I during the day, had to hold the fort. And fort it was, an armed encampment.

Tony would come home from school and sit in front of the television. For the first time his work fell off; his interim report card was the first poor one in a lifetime of A's. But instead of studying, he sat in front of the television, brooding rather than seeing.

No one dared come into the room. When one of the other children ventured in, there would be a shout of rage: *Get the hell out of here!* And they got out, because there was nothing I could do except to beg them to keep away from Tony. And they knew there was nothing I could do.

He no longer came to the table to eat with the family. He waited until we were all finished and then helped himself in the refrigerator. He refused to touch any food that I had prepared or handled; even a bakery cake, if my hand had untied the string. Not until years later did we hear he was afraid his food was being poisoned.

We were floundering. I found myself, in my desperation, quarreling with Jack.

"Will you find a place for him, get him out of this house? What kind of father can watch his family die by inches like this? You're a doctor. Can't you do something, anything?"

It was most unfair, because Jack was as helpless and frightened as I.

Then at last we came to the place I shall call The School. I do not

12

know why Dr. Collins allowed us to flounder so long, but one day when I called him after weeks of dispiriting search, he asked if we had tried The School. "It's about the best there is," he said, and promised to write and send them a preliminary report so they would be prepared for our interview.

It was a welcoming place. Despite all our apprehensions and overwhelming sense of defeat as we sat in the waiting room, we felt that instantly.

Memory plays strange tricks. I don't know what made me think, while we waited there, of the day we had been married. How the world had glittered that day! If you loved each other and worked hard, if you were loyal and honest, life would reward you. It is just as well we could not have known the strange places to which life would bring us.

I looked secretly at the other faces in the waiting room. There was a handsome young couple with a look of security and position. Surely they never expected to be sitting here! Then an older couple, gray, shabby and genteel, she in a clean cotton dress and worn gloves; apparently life had not been easy for them, and you could tell they were bewildered, as if to ask why the extra burden had been put upon them.

Finally we were directed to a pleasant man, the psychiatric social worker who would listen to our story. He had already gone over the papers on his desk, the history of Tony sent by Dr. Collins.

We shook hands. "Our doctors have gone over all this," he told us, indicating the papers. "If you are still interested after we have answered all your questions, I believe we will accept Tony. He seems to be a child we might help."

And he explained, "We do not accept psychotic children here. Only the emotionally disturbed, those with behavior problems. We offer a tightly structured environment, with highly individual attention. The ratio of staff to students is three to one."

We sat there carefully listening and yet not really considering. We had already made up our minds. This was the place. There was an unmistakable warmth about the comfortable brick ivy-covered houses which lay scattered over the enormous meadows and sheltered behind old trees. At a bend in the driveway we had seen a pond where boys could swim in the summer and skate in the winter; from where we now sat we could hear cries from a ballfield across the lane. The slap of tennis balls came from the courts just below the windows.

13

". . . no one is ever left alone to sink into depression or get into trouble. Every minute is accounted for, between study and recreation. The staff people work in conjunction with whatever psychiatrist is attending any particular boy."

"What is the average length of stay?" Jack inquired.

"Anywhere from one to three years. It's hard to give an average. By the time we are through with them, which is by the time they have completed the high-school course, they are ready to go to college or to work or to whatever place in life the individual is fitted for."

Hope, irrepressible, began rising inside me again. "In other words, most of the boys really turn out well?"

"Yes, I would say so. You may wonder what it is we do. No magic, I assure you. But you see, by taking the boy out of the home where the whole family is so emotionally involved, and raising him in the care of impartial, trained people, we can inculcate a whole new set of living habits. It is a conditioning process which no parent, however skilled, devoted or intelligent could possibly effect."

That made sense.

"And so often at home these children resist psychotherapy. Here there is no choice about going. It is part of the weekly routine, like meals, basketball practice or math class. I note here that Tony has not seen his psychiatrist for the past few months."

"No, we have not been able to make him go. We're really in a pretty bad situation at home."

A sympathetic nod. "I can imagine. It can be rough on the family. What does Tony think about coming here? You've discussed it with him, of course?"

"Well, one doesn't *discuss* anything with Tony at this point. We told him, we informed him, that we were looking into this as a possibility. And he has flatly refused to have anything to do with it."

"He won't come?"

"No, I really don't know what we're going to do," Jack said, "if we can't persuade him."

"I suppose he will have to be brought forcibly."

"I suppose so. My brother, maybe," Jack said. There was a miserable silence, thinking about that, and then Jack asked, "May we discuss the fee?"

"Oh yes. It is high. It has to be, for what we give. The fee is six hundred dollars a month."

It did not mean a thing to me at that moment. If he had said six

14

thousand dollars a month I think it would have made no more impression on me. All I knew was that we had found a place to take Tony, people to help him, and we would have rest.

They were to make room for Tony the following week. That was the longest week in my life. I literally counted the hours. The tension in our house built up so that it seemed surely something, someone, might burst open.

Yet the very night before we were to go, Jack would have changed his mind. Neither of us could sleep. We sat up late, whispering. Jack wanted reassurance, desperately. "Are we doing the right thing, Louise? Should we try longer?"

I threw up my hands. "How can we ask it of ourselves? Or of the children?

"I don't know. And yet—we have to give Tony every chance. We owe it to him."

"Jack, maybe they'll help him at The School. I feel so strongly that they will. We aren't doing a thing for him here."

"That's true."

We took Tony in the morning. Quietly, so that he would not hear and suspect, Russell [Jack's brother] and another man, the only other one who knew our story, parked their car down at the end of the driveway and entered by the back door, which had been left open for them.

Tony had to be taken bodily from his room, kicking, screaming, and most terrible of all, cursing Jack and me for putting him out of his home. Jane and the twins had already left for school and mercifully were spared the scene. Hanna hid in the kitchen, wringing her hands. The two men got Tony into the back seat of the car between them; Jack drove. I drove the second car alone with all the luggage.

And so Tony left home.

I suppose we were all, in a sense, numb that day. But The School held forth such hopes to us. Though I had not figured out how, I truly believed that somehow they would know something no one else had known. I believed that in a year or two Tony would be straightened out; that he would come home and go to school and live with the family in peace. If I had known how it was to be I would surely not have been able to get through that day as steadily as I did.

I drove the car two hundred miles, to The School. I met the staff and said the ordinary things. I knew what the right behavior must be. I knew I must manage for Jack's sake. Also, I must confess I had some

15

feeling of relief, just the sheer physical relief of having a burden taken from me. That night I would go home and shut my door and be able to sleep all through one night.

We came home, exhausted and emptied. We sat down to dinner with our children. It was the first, sane, quiet dinner hour in years.

The children talked of their own affairs; not a word about their brother was said. They were so young, and surely they could not understand the whole truth of what had happened. Yet I knew that they were aware that something deeply moving had taken place, and tactfully were trying to help their father and mother.

When we had almost finished dessert, Jack spoke. "We are all thinking of Tony tonight. He's in a good place, a school where they will help him get over his troubles. After a while," he said smiling at the three still faces, "he will be coming back to us."

There was no comment and presently they all excused themselves to do their homework. Right afterward Jack and I went to our room and fell asleep.

It was at least a week later that I really understood what had happened. I was driving one forenoon toward the shopping center and there ahead of me on Maple Avenue I saw a boy. The shape and walk were so familiar that I thought absently: what is Tony doing out of school? Then I remembered; blind with tears, I had to stop the car. At last I knew my heart was broken.

Soon after, Tony wrote us a letter beseeching us to take him home. Jack answered it carefully. Very lovingly, he explained why it would be best for him to stay where he was for the time being. Tony's answering letter was a tirade of furious threats and hatred. Then no more letters came; there was silence.

c. 1956

2

"Conspiracy Against the Weak"

DAVID VISCOTT

A family argument turns into a wrestling match that ends with seventeen-year-old Peter being sent to a psychiatric ward by ambulance. Despite efforts of Dr. Viscott, his supervisor Jerry Gelb, and fellow resident Bert Feinstein, "research" ensnares Peter, and face-saving maneuvers prolong the teenager's stay.

SOME OF the admissions to Bamberg 5 were ridiculous. They often resulted from people losing control and picking on the most vulnerable member of their family, labeling him sick and sending him to the hospital as a human sacrifice to solve everyone else's problems.

Anyhow that was the way it seemed with Peter Atkins. Peter was seventeen and had growing pains. He was continually arguing with his mother over the proper length of his hair, fighting with his father over the use of the family car, and battling with his younger brother over anything at all. His brother also fought with his parents just about as frequently.

One evening, all the other members of the family formally declared war on Peter. Peter and his brother were fighting over the ownership of a particular sports jacket Peter planned to wear on a date that night. Father wasn't sure Peter should have the car since he hadn't cut the lawn as he had promised. Nor had he cut his hair, so mother also joined the fun.

Understandably Peter felt outnumbered. Father called in a next-

17

door neighbor, Dr. Blade, a local surgeon who knew Peter well. Dr. Blade came over and tried to calm Peter down. He gave him advice based on what Peter's father, never one for objectivity, told him on the phone. Peter told the good doctor to "fuck off" because Peter had a date.

Dr. Blade told the family, "That's not like Peter I know. Something has changed. He may be having an emotional break." Another reason why I love surgeons—at times like this they all seem to act like a Back Passage.

Peter grabbed the disputed sports jacket and headed for the door. Dr. Blade shouted, "Don't let him out." Father and brother pounced on him and held him down. While he was being held down on the Oriental rug in the entrance hall, he started to cry, something he hadn't done in years. That stopped them. At Dr. Blade's suggestion (prompted by his guilt?) Peter was taken by ambulance to Bamberg 5. By ambulance! Can you believe that? I wanted to ask Mr. Atkins when Peter arrived why he didn't have a police escort. I'm sure Atkins would have told me that Dr. Blade didn't think of it. Would someone please check if Blue Cross covers police escorts?

I had no choice but to admit Peter overnight because the situation at home was so overheated. I opened our session by saying "I've already heard your father's, your mother's, and your brother's side of the story—all at once. If you've been through what they put me through you probably could use a vacation from them." Peter looked clobbered but he managed to smile. After Peter told me his story I said, "Well, this is the mistake of the century. When do you want to go home? How's tomorrow morning?"

"Home?" he said, startled. "I can go home?"

"Sure, there's nothing wrong with you," I said, getting up from my chair. "Want a pizza?"

Peter stared at me disbelievingly, but eventually managed to put away two pizzas at Primo's Pizza down the street. He liked them large, with extra cheese and without anchovies. Peter, after all, was a growing boy. We talked and cleared the air. By the time we got back to the ward Peter at least felt someone understood him. He was completely relaxed, although somewhat thirsty. Helen Doran, who adored adolescents, gave him a quart of milk, which he gulped down from the cardboard container in one swig, in classic locker-room-after-winning-the-big-game style. Peter asked for some cookies to wash down the milk.

"It's great to see a normal kid on the ward for a change," said

Helen, loud enough for Peter to hear, and handed him a box of cookies. "Leave at least one for someone else," she added. Peter left two. "Besides being normal, he's also generous," said Helen pursing her lips.

Carol Downs, the psychiatric social worker, appeared on the ward. It was nine thirty. Why is she here? I wondered. "I was asked to speak with you about the Atkins family," said Carol. "I would like to see the Atkinses and evaluate each family member individually and then together as a family unit later. It's a new program in the social service department. We'll be seeing the family of each new patient as well as the patient from the time of admission. We'll follow them through the hospitalization all the way to discharge and in follow-up visits after discharge."

"Sure, but you'd better hurry, Carol, because this kid is going to be discharged tomorrow so he can make Saturday morning baseball practice."

"You can't do that without a formal presentation!" Carol protested. "This is a new program. My supervisor and the head of the psychiatric social worker training program will be at the presentation. It's important. I've been assigned to the case. We need a minimum of fifteen case studies to meet the requirements of the grant."

"Well, you'll have to evaluate the Atkinses on an outpatient basis."

"No, I can't. We need at least one week in the hospital to determine an emotional baseline."

"Well, this patient isn't going to be here a week. So he isn't suitable. And I think your study is unscientific." (I shouldn't have said that.)

"Well, he can't be discharged without a workup," Carol said. "That's *standard operating procedure.*" Carol was pulling protocol and at a loose end in her cardigan. Here it was a warm May night and she was still wearing a sweater!

"This kid shouldn't have been admitted." I practically shouted. "I won't compound one error by making another. I'm writing an order to discharge him tomorrow."

I did.

The next morning I told Bert what was going on and left the hospital at nine. Tough luck, Bert, having duty on a weekend as beautiful as this.

When I came in on Monday I found Peter Atkins waiting for me at the nurses' station.

"What the hell are you doing here?" I asked.

19

"They changed your order."

"Can I see you?" said Bert, who apparently was also waiting for me to appear. "It's about this case."

"Come on, Peter, you're going to sit in on this."

"Good for you, David," called out Jackie Rose as we walked to my office. "Let the kid know what's happening."

Bert sat in my chair. I sat on the desk. Peter sat in the patient's chair.

"Carol Downs," Bert began, his chair squeaking like crazy, "called her supervisor, who called Dr. Noyes, and Dr. Noyes rescinded your order."

"On what authority?" I demanded, forgetting Bert was on my side.

"He made up some bullshit about it being too impulsive a decision and that an adequate evaluation was not possible in that short a time."

"Maybe not enough time for Noyes to evaluate an adolescent, because no adolescent I know would talk to that authoritarian son of a bitch."

"We got along just great," Peter said. "You guys have the same bullshit here that I get at home."

"The kid's got a point," Bert said. "Did you have breakfast?" he asked, inviting Peter to join him in the coffee shop. *Everyone* could tell Peter was OK.

I walked by Dr. Noyes' office and asked to see him. Field Marshall von Noyes happened to be free. As a matter of fact, his secretary said he *wanted* to see me.

"Ah, yes," Dr. Noyes began, "I hear there was some sort of misunderstanding this weekend. You know Dr. Michael Blade, the surgeon, don't you? A fine man. A fine surgeon, and one of the most respected people on the medical school staff. An excellent teacher— excellent. Well, when one of our own, so to speak, sends us a patient, I think we owe it to him to give the patient as professional a workup as we know how, don't you? We must not act impulsively. It's not only bad practice, but it gives the department a bad name. Also, there is a departmental study for which, according to the descriptions of the case I have received, this boy and family would be excellent candidates. I'd like to see that we get a good baseline of family-patient interaction for the study. You do agree, don't you?"

"No, I—"

"Are you so confident of what you casually observed about this

20

young man during a time of crisis, when his entire family was confused and he was in turmoil, that you would discharge him after so short a time? In my opinion that is very poor judgment. Very poor indeed. We don't discharge patients unless they've been properly evaluated."

"He was evaluated," I said.

"By you," Noyes stated.

"Yes, by me. This boy was—"

"I am quite familiar with his story. I spoke with the head of social service."

"But she didn't see the patient!"

"No, but Miss Downs saw the family."

"Do you mean that a decision based on the firsthand experience of a resident trained in your program with a patient is going to be overruled by people who never saw the patient? That's the craziest thing I ever heard of."

"That patient must be evaluated before discharge," Noyes said, restating his position. "And Dr. Viscott, if you have any comments or opinions you will keep them to yourself. We don't want to appear anti-research."

I called Jerry Gelb as soon as I got out of Noyes' office. You can't win an argument against Noyes, and I was afraid that if I tried he'd hold it against me and be vindictive enough to ruin my references.

Jerry was sympathetic to my argument. He saw Peter Atkins, agreed with me, and was willing to sign a discharge order. Peter Atkins left; Carol Downs called her supervisor; and M. Austin Noyes called Jerry and me in on the carpet.

"What do you have to say, Dr. Viscott?"

"I don't think he needs to say anything," said Jerry. "I saw the Atkins boy. I read the admission note. I know Dr. Viscott, and I trust his judgment. The standard I used, Austin, was simple. I asked myself, if the boy were my private patient would I keep him in the hospital. The answer was I would not. I didn't think the boy even needed an appointment for a follow-up visit. To keep him in the hospital unjustifiably would only have given him more ammunition to use against his parents and make it more difficult for him to come to terms with them later on."

"I think the boy should stay here, Jerry," Noyes repeated. "I said as much."

"But you didn't talk with him," Jerry pointed out.

21

"I'm planning to see him on Wednesday. I have a meeting with the Planning Committee for the new mental health center on Mondays."

Noyes had not been terribly active treating patients for several years. He rarely saw patients as far as I could tell. He was an administrative psychiatrist, a political. He wrote a lot of articles, enjoyed an excellent reputation and was involved in a lot of departmental infighting. He arranged university appointments for the people he liked and was active in the politics and planning of community mental health facilities. He often carried blueprints with him to conferences. It got to the point where I felt I was taking a graduate course in architecture. I suspected he saw the Governor more frequently than he saw any patient, especially an adolescent patient like Peter.

No one in the department really seemed to like Dr. Noyes, and many psychiatrists, supposedly even some grown-up psychoanalysts, were afraid of him. Amazing. Or maybe not, if you had certain ambitions.

M. Austin Noyes stopped and looked at both of us, as if he expected us to understand how much more important his appointment was than this trivial matter.

"Wednesday's a long time for a kid who wants to be out playing baseball," I said.

"Young people are remarkably resilient, Dr. Viscott. A few days in the hospital will not be as upsetting to him as you think. And certainly not as disruptive as the rebellion I'd have between this department and social services and the department of surgery. You've made Dr. Blade appear like an ass."

I kept my big mouth shut for a change, and walked out with Jerry. Jerry sighed. "I was sure you were going to say something." He was almost right.

c. 1966

3

"Where They Can Force People to Stay"

DAKIN WILLIAMS

When Dakin Williams received a phone call from his frightened brother Tennessee in Florida, he went out to join him immediately and suggested that the playwright enter a hospital. They flew to St. Louis the same night, and Tennessee checked into Barnes Hospital a day later. He tried to walk out when the staff took away the sedatives and liquor he had been using regularly, but Dakin quickly arranged to have him sedated and committed to the hospital's psychiatric division. Dakin didn't tell him that he could leave after ten days. Tennessee ended up staying two months. Furious, he later had Dakin's power of attorney rescinded, and he adjusted his will so that his brother would get nothing.

Dakin tells of visiting his brother on the evening of his admission to Barnes Hospital and the aftermath.

"I WENT by that evening and he was sitting up in the Queeney Tower. He had his bottle of booze and his bag of pills, and he looked like he had the world by the tail. Everything was fine. But the hospital was just making routine tests. The next day they came to some conclusions about him. They took away the booze and the pills. Tennessee did what he always does—he started to walk out. I'd sent him a big bouquet of flowers in hopes of getting a nice welcome, but he was furious with me. The doctor was there—a neurologist—and he was going to just let him walk out. So I said to myself, 'Good God, I've got him this far, I'm not going to let him leave if I can help it.' I got hold of another doctor I knew—he had treated Mother—and he said, 'If Dakin will take the responsibility, he can sign him in for ten days, even against his will.' So he thought when he went to the elevator that he was going to New York, but the intern got behind him and inoculated him with something in his arm that put him to sleep, and he woke up in the only place in the hospital where they can force people to stay—Renard, the psychiatric division. I understand that when he woke up he looked around and said, 'Where am I, the Plaza?'

"I didn't see him for three days because he was so infuriated. He also had three convulsions coming off the Doriden. He nearly died. The doctors said so. I was there every day except when he would get angry at me. Then I'd stay away for two or three days to pacify him. After a while he became very friendly and very much himself. I hadn't seen him that way in several years; I'd almost forgotten what it was like. Y'know what one of the doctors told him? 'Tennessee, if you play ball with us, you'll write better than you ever wrote in your life.' That was very clever, I thought, motivating him like that. After that first month he stayed in voluntarily the second month. He could've gotten out in ten days if he had known his legal rights, but I didn't tell him."

1969

"The Kidnapping"

EARL LONG

Earl Long had served as governor of Louisiana from 1939 to 1940 and 1948 to 1952. He was nearing the end of his third term in 1959 when he unsuccessfully tried to stay in office in spite of a state law prohibiting consecutive terms. "Feeling his power slip away, the governor upbraided first a House committee and then a joint session. Pausing only to sip bourbon from a soft-drink bottle, he loosed a stream of profanity and invective that appalled his listeners," read his obituary in *The New York Times* on September 6, 1960.

A few days after that performance, following a night of bargaining at the Executive Mansion that involved both doctors and politicians, Long was heavily sedated and flown in a National Guard plane to Galveston, Texas, where his wife committed him to a mental hospital. There he was diagnosed "paranoid schizophrenic." He implored her to sign him out. She did, on the condition that he submit to psychiatric treatment in Louisiana. But Long stalked out of Louisiana's Oshner Foundation Hospital the day after he entered and sped toward Baton Rouge, in a state police car. Mrs. Long had a commitment order drawn up. As the governor approached the state capital, he was seized and placed in Mandeville State Hospital. His aides engineered his release nine days later by calling a meeting of the Long-controlled State Hospital Board, which fired Mandeville's two chief administrators and replaced them with men who certified the governor sane. As Allen Ginsberg has written, "Sanity a trick of agreement."

"THEY MISLED me. The reason I was feeling so poorly at the last Legislature was I had kept on postponing an operation that I was to have at the Oshner Clinic in New Orleans. When my sweet little wife and my dear little nephew got me to go on that plane, they told me a damn lie that I was going to Oshner for my operation.

"Then when they got me to the plane the bonecrushers strapped me to the stretcher and a doctor stuck me through the britches with a needle. My wife and nephew promised they would come right down to Oshner next day to see me. But the plane flew me to Galveston, and my sweet little wife hasn't shown up yet, neither my little nephew. When the plane landed me at that airport, there, they told me I was going to a rest house, where I was promised a double bed and quiet. The doctors gave me pills to make me sleep. First I took them one by one, then by the papercupful. Then I got to chunkin' them in there by the wad. While I was in that condition, they got me to sign a thing that I wouldn't sue them for kidnapping. I went contrary to what my lawyers would have wanted. . . .

"They snatched me out without even enough clothes on me to cover up a red bug and a week after I arrived in Texas I was enjoying the same wardrobe. They put me in a room with the door open and crazy people walking in and out all night; one of them thought it was the toilet. . . .

"Then, this Corner here. Wasn't he a nice judge to commit me to Mandeville when I come back? We been on opposite sides in politics as long as I remember, but if the position had been reversed, I might have given him a break. And Bankston, the superintendent, a man I appointed myself, could have left me out, but he wouldn't. But I got out, all right. I put *him* out and *got* out."

1959

5

"What's the Verdict?"

JANET GOTKIN

Reacting to the sadness and anger in her life, Janet Gotkin slashed her wrists time and again. After a failed suicide attempt at the first series of hospitals to which she was sent, she feels that her doctor had ". . . said, in effect, 'If you continue to act in accordance with your deepest feelings, we will send you away to a state institution. If you stop acting on the truth of your despair, we will give you your freedom.'" Like the mental hospital inmate who protests, "I am not crying because I am crazy, but because I am sad,"[1] Gotkin refuses to consider herself sick. She understands the threat of indefinite institutionalization and alienation in the sickness label: "Maybe I am sick, but if it is a sickness, it has become me, and I am no longer like the rest of the people I knew and know. My world is hounded by mental hospitals, doctors, drugs, and shock treatments. These people who say they want to help me have turned me into— into—an outsider. I have never been so alone in my life."

This selection takes place in the doctor's office, three days after Janet has slashed her wrists in his office, and prior to her first hospitalization. When her father asks the psychiatrist what the verdict is, he's expressing the widespread belief that psychiatrists have the right to pass judgment.

MY PARENTS and I had our final interview with Dr. Berman three days later. We huddled in our circle of easy chairs while the doctor sat ensconced behind his fortresslike desk. The scene was eerily reminiscent of our first meeting; only this time my sentence would no doubt be stiffer. The crime had been greater.

27

"Well, what's the verdict?" my father asked numbly.

"She must, of course, be hospitalized as soon as possible. I have tried to help her," Dr. Berman said gravely. "But, as you can see," he added, gesturing toward my still-bandaged wrists, "she has been most unresponsive and uncooperative."

"Of course," my parents mumbled. It was almost automatic, their agreement.

If Dr. Berman, from his heights of professional wisdom, had prescribed joining a chain gang to "cure" my illness, I think my parents might have consented. Would the doctor do anything to hurt their daughter? Didn't the doctor know best? Wasn't the psychiatrist privy to information about his patient that the lay person couldn't begin to understand? This wasn't a matter of choice; it was a question of a sick person and a doctor's informed diagnosis and prescription. Wasn't it?

Of course.

My parents must have had their doubts about putting me in a hospital; just as they must have had their doubts about the wisdom of my five-times-a-week psychoanalysis. But they respected achievement and professional expertise. To have admitted their doubts would have been to open a chink in the iron edifice of psychiatric ominiscience. Then what would they do? Flounder and drown. And I might still be in pain and confusion and distress. Love might say, "Don't lock her up"; but what did love know? The expert said, "Lock her up." The doctor had to know best. The doctor always knew best. I was sick. I was mentally ill. I needed "help."

They were desolate, inconsolable, so deep in their own pain and self-doubt they barely saw me at all. Horrified by the depth of my despair, unable to face the implications of my misery, they wallowed in guilt and helplessness, gratefully embracing Dr. Berman's considered professional judgment.

No one asked me what I wanted to do, if anything; where I wanted to go, if anywhere.

The unanimous opinion was that my opinion, if I had one, was worthless. The moment I lifted my hand against myself, the instant I violated the suicide taboo, I relinquished all rights to speak in my own behalf.

No one questioned for an instant the assumption that my violence against myself was irrational and "sick." No one asked, for even a moment, if that act of desperate self-destruction could have been a

28

logical reaction to a barren, dead-end, lonely life. That was unthinkable.

Dr. Berman hid his anger under the cloak of objective psychiatric evaluation and sent me away with a smirk and a sigh of relief.

"I don't know if I can do it," he said vaguely, "but I'll try to get her on the emergency list at Oceanville Hospital. There's usually a three-month wait, but . . ."

My parents looked waxen, miserable, melted small from the tensions of the situation. They looked at me, their looks filled with pleas for understanding, reassurance, forgiveness. I couldn't blame them, but I couldn't support them in their decision, either. We were all on our own.

I listened to them making plans for my life. They were terrified, I realized, by the single physical fact of the cuts on my wrists.

"Haven't they ever wanted to hurt themselves?" I wondered. "Everyone does, sometime or other. The only difference is, I *did* it."

They were so terrified they wanted to get me put away quickly so they wouldn't have to face their own madness and violence as it was mirrored on my arms.

My mother and father wanted me to feel glad again—they loved me. But they could not cope with the explicitness of my desperation. They thought I would get help in the hospital. They were innocents; they had no real reason for believing otherwise.

Dr. Berman, on the other hand, was speaking of other things when he assured my parents I would get the help I so urgently needed. When I emerged from the hospital, I would no longer cut my wrists; I would be helped. Subliminally, if not consciously, my parents must have understood his message and been glad. Glad for me; but glad for themselves.

The interview was over. Dr. Berman shook hands with me. I watched his eyes darting covertly back to my forbidden wrists. He looked guilty, as if he was afraid his mama was going to discover him looking at dirty pictures.

That weekend my father received a call. Dr. Berman had worked with speed and efficiency; his influence had never served him better. Two weeks later he was through with me and the threat of blood on the carpets forever.

I entered Oceanville Hospital, Belville, New York, in Spring, 1962. My career as a full-fledged mental patient had begun.

1962

6

"The Letdown"

SARAH E. LORENZ

rs. Lorenz and husband Cleve take rooms for themselves on a psychiatric ward in preparation for the transfer from another hospital of their nineteen-year-old son, Ken, who is "obsessive-compulsive." Her overconfidence in "research" gradually changes into a feeling of being caught up in something terrible. See the Treatment section for the continuation of her account.

WE HAD driven through the lovely grounds of that immense and imposing center built like a city in itself. We had pulled up before a towering building and climbed out, two tense, tired people, our spirits clinging to the tail end of a star. Inside, we gazed about as we waited for an elevator. The huge lobby, bright, bustling, modern, seemed symbolic of all mankind's struggle for light, for knowledge. Men and women in spanking white coats walked briskly about, some of them in earnest conversation, others obliviously reading a "paper" that was perhaps the summation of months or years of digging, exploring.

Researchers are a unique breed, in the main a dedicated, selfless lot. Their intellectual curiosity gives them vitality, an air of promise that shines forth like a beacon, exuding a hopefulness, an air of expectation to which the most heavyhearted must respond. We were to meet and talk with many of these men, and always their effect was to renew our faith that, given enough time, tools, and money, there was almost no problem that could not be solved. That faith has not diminished, and we certainly felt it strongly then.

We took the elevator to the third floor and pushed through

swinging doors to another brightly appointed lobby. Through another door that stood (significantly, for us) wide open, we walked resolutely into the unit we were henceforth to know as home. Our hearts were beating wildly, and we both felt a sensation akin to prayer.

The head nurse greeted us with cordial reserve and introduced us to other members of the staff. We had learned by now that several families were participating in the project, and I looked forward to meeting them. Here, like Ken, we would not be alone in our strange environment. There would be other families who shared the common denominator of a son's or daughter's mental illness. I looked forward to good companionship with people whose mutual problems should make for a mutually satisfying communal living experience. For me this was of real concern.

But no family member was visible, to my vague disquiet. The unit, except for the nursing staff, was quiet. Too quiet. Where was everyone?

The head nurse left to make arrangements for bringing our belongings up. Two aides pushing a huge supply cart appeared, and Cleve went out with them to help. Since no room was assigned to us as yet, our things were to be stored in one of the sleeping rooms until our return the following week. It proved to be a starkly forbidding, tiled room, which, the nurse hastily explained, had originally been built as a seclusion room for highly disturbed patients; in this project it would be used as a bedroom. I cringed as the nurse turned a key in the lock, securing the door.

She then showed us about the unit, pointing out the family dining and living areas, the play and all-purpose room, treatment room for physical ailments, and the small kitchen used for evening snacks. A newness and brightness prevailed, almost blotting out the grim tiled bedroom.

"I'd like to show you a typical family bedroom," she said, knocking gently on a door.

A small, wan, tired-looking man appeared, brightening at sight of us. "You're the new family. Welcome!" The greeting was sincere and warm; already a kinship of sorts was established.

At the nurse's, "May we show the folks your room?" he cordially invited us in. We saw a spacious, tastefully appointed room, painted a cheerful yellow, with attractive contemporary furnishings, and cozy with personal belongings. It might have been a room in a modern new apartment building. Although compaining of a headache, Mr. Daly was hospitable and friendly and seemed especially pleased that Cleve would be present on the unit.

"I hope Mrs. Daly will be up before you leave. She's down at the beauty shop with our daughter Linda."

Back in the large, comfortable living room, I gathered from talk among some of the nurses and attendants, that only a short while before our arrival Linda had been involved in a violent incident in the lobby. As Mr. Daly subdued her, she had struck him, knocking off his glasses and breaking them. No doubt this explained his severe headache.

While we were still trying to take this in, Mrs. Daly and Linda appeared, freshly coiffured from the beauty parlor. I was totally unprepared for Linda's loveliness. I could only gaze at her, confounded, trying to relate this tall blonde exquisite creature to the incident just described. She was dainty; she was gracious; she had a poise and a classic beauty that bordered on elegance . . . until you saw the vague glassiness of her eyes and the vacancy of her smile. "How do you do," she murmured charmingly. And then oddly, "Thank you very much!"

Mrs. Daly was lovely, too, in a small, blonde, eager way. She welcomed us as warmly as her husband; we were drawn to her at once. But never have I seen such dark circles as those that rimmed her eyes. It was as if they had been drawn there, indelible reminders of some long and terrible ordeal.

Next Molly, an exuberant eighteen-year-old girl, joined us, walking in at her half-skipping little gait. She was a plump, rosily attractive young person, who greeted us with winning enthusiasm. Plumping down cozily beside us, she plucked a cigarette from a trim plastic case, tapped it expertly on the arm of the chair, and chattered amiably away . . . about friends of hers who were patients in other units and about practically everybody on the staff. Then she branched off into everything from TV programs to marriage, revealing an amusing mixture of sophistication and naivete.

"Wow, a man on the unit!" she laughed, demanding his vital statistics when we told her about Ken. It all seemed so natural, so everyday that I found myself thinking what a happy companion for Ken she'd be.

At this point Mrs. Goodman, Molly's mother, came swooping down on us. She was a distinguished-looking woman in her early fifties, smartly dressed, with considerable costume jewelry and the air of a charm-school hostess. "I know! You're the new family . . . how wonderful!" she cried, her hand held high in rapturous greeting. In an aside, she whispered cryptically, "You can thank me for voting you in."

And I did. "I'm glad to meet you, too," I said, meaning it.

She didn't hear; she was already plying us with personal questions, mixed with a rain of incredible flattery. Totally bewildered and acutely uncomfortable, I was rescued by the appearance of a uniformed maid, wheeling a coffee cart; Mrs. Goodman sailed off suddenly toward the refreshment tray.

Claire, the head nurse, had baked a batch of cookies as a special treat. (Already we had been told to call the staff by their first names.) Claire was a tall, rather gaunt, but immaculate person with auburn hair, long-nosed, thin-lipped, exquisitely groomed, wearing street dress rather than uniform. She seemed the perfect hostess as she poured, and I looked happily about, feeling like the guest at a gay afternoon party. The room with its modern decor was so comfortable, so appealing; the group seemed to enjoy such a casual camaraderie. What an environment for an ill person, I marveled. What a change from the usual stark hospital atmosphere.

Audrey Prout, another young patient-member, joined us, a slim attractive girl with a clean town-and-country look. Her mother would not be arriving for a week or two, and in the interim Audrey would be on her own. I wondered what was wrong with Audrey. As with Molly, there was no distinct evidence of illness. An aloofness, a reticence, yes, but illness? None that I could see. And I pondered on the strangeness of this, the many faces of illness that, like the many faces of human nature, are as varied and complex as the people themselves.

As I regarded Audrey, this wholesome, well-built young woman, I wondered about the problems, the circumstances that had brought her to the institute. She appeared oblivious to our presence until someone mentioned Ken; then, as Molly had done, she brightened perceptibly. She warmed to us still more when she learned that we came from her own state. We were mistaken about her reticence; she had a refreshing candor that cut at once through the usual social stiffness on first contact. This lack of inhibition is a characteristic that often distinguishes the mentally ill from the normal, so-called. The facade, the false veneer, is stripped away. If only one could retain the

33

honest emotion of the ill, I have sometimes thought, and throw to the winds the pretensions, the ambiguities that distort our relations with other people. If only one could maintain this in proper balance, how different out lives might be.

There was to be a clinical meeting at three, and we waited with interest for it to start. Precisely at five minutes of three, aides and family members arranged the chairs to make an informal circle. By three everyone was seated, chatting much as any group would. Precisely on the hour, Dr. Cohane, the director, and Dr. Dimmock walked in. We had not seen Dr. Cohane during the past six months, and I was eager to greet him and thank him for our presence here today. I waited for some sign of recognition as the group quieted and the doctors sat down. Then I would go to him.

However, such terms as "patient-centered," "patient-directed," "objective professional stance" were not yet within my scope of comprehension. Thus what ensued was completely baffling. Dr. Cohane greeted no one. His expression was immobile, deadpan. Once he peered about the room, and I tried to catch his eye. But a curt nod to Cleve and me—evidently a major concession—discouraged any further familiarity. Convinced that he recognized us, I waited for the moment when we'd at least be officially welcomed into the "family." I was not looking for special treatment, but a word of acknowledgment, an introduction, seemed only civilized. But none came, not from him or Dr. Dimmock or the head nurse Claire or the social worker who'd interviewed us earlier. Not from anybody. The climate felt so cool, so indifferent as to be apathetic. Nervously I glanced at Cleve, wondering how he was reacting. He above all must retain his enthusiasm. But Cleve's expression, too, was noncommittal, as if he had caught the strange contagion.

Feeling hollow in the pit of my stomach, I sat as silent as the rest. Why didn't somebody call the meeting to order? What in the world could be holding things up? Surely they weren't waiting for Cleve or me to speak! I looked at Dr. Cohane, half expecting some clue, but as far as he was concerned we were not even there.

Silence can invite meditation, reflection. It can be calming, tranquilizing, acting as water or sunshine to draw out roots of thought, inviting them to blossom. But not this silence . . . it was harsh and cold, almost ominous. Everyone sat as rigid as zombies, including the nurses, and I wondered about their being here. The whole performance was so mystifying it was like being onstage in some grotesque play. Its meaning escaped me.

Occasionally there was movement. Once Mr. Daly changed positions and lit a cigarette. So did Mrs. Daly. Now maybe someone would speak. No one did, but there was a chain reaction; others began to shift about in their chairs, to light cigarettes. Mrs. Goodman nervously fingered her many-stranded pearls. But still no one spoke, and the heavy tension was not relieved until Linda suddenly stood up. All eyes followed her as she walked over to her father, asking in her innocently appealing, childlike voice, "May I have a cigarette, Daddy? Thank you very much," she added mechanically.

The eyes followed her as she strolled over to the full-length mirror, where she stood in narcissistic contemplation, turning the better to admire herself, lifting her arms, pirouetting, smiling, laughing hollowly. It was sad and startling, this lovely creature lost in her own dream world, but it furnished a form of weird relief.

Surely someone will call her back, I thought. But no one did. Then all of a sudden she walked briskly to her seat, plunged her face in her hands, and crouched there, locked away. The silence continued, the long, long silence that began to beat as loud as a thunderous drum. Speak up! Somebody, say something, I wanted to shout, and I looked at Cleve, hoping he would speak, make some witty comment about the silence . . . anything. But Cleve sat as mute as the others. Then it dawned on me: this must be their way of inviting relaxation, trying to put people at ease. Naively I made myself more comfortable, sighing audibly. This only turned all eyes in my direction, as if they expected me now to speak.

Everything comes to an end eventually. It was Mr. Daly who finally was the first to give up in what seemed like a grim game in which everybody strove to outlast the others. He cleared his throat. Choosing his words carefully, pacing them as slowly as if they were to be held up for inspection by a board of censors, he announced: "Since our guests will be joining us next week and Mrs. Prout will be coming shortly, this might be as good a time as any to get the room situation in shape."

Thank heaven, I thought, blissfully unaware that these innocent words would precipitate a small-scale war. I listened intently, wondering what rooms would be assigned to our family.

Mrs. Goodman promptly took up the cudgels. Fidgeting with her jewelry, she declared her opposition to the proposed changes. Moving two females back into one room instead of the two they now occupied was unthinkable. "Why, with all Molly's clothes," she said, her anxiety rising, "I wouldn't have room to turn around!"

35

Claire's appraisal of the situation went unheeded. The ideas that flew back and forth only agitated Mrs. Goodman further. She repeated her earlier objections, injecting a note of suspicion. Everyone was picking on her, the Dalys, the head nurse, everybody. The Dalys, she insisted, would get what they wanted as usual. She, as usual, would be left out in the cold. Evidently a few rooms were favored over others. All but two had adjoining baths, and this, too, seemed a factor in the heated exchange.

Since agreement seemed remote, the head nurse suggested forming a committee to attempt to arrive at an equitable solution. And directly after the meeting, the committee, composed of Mrs. Daly, Mrs. Goodman, Audrey, and Cleve, adjourned to a near-by room. Fifteen minutes later they filed out like a jury arrived at a verdict, outwardly amicable over the decision, Mrs. Goodman apparently appeased.

Arrangements began for the necessary moves. When shown the room which would next week be ours, Cleve and I were pleased. However, the room that now held our belongings, the room that had chilled us on sight, had been assigned to Ken. The only compensating factor was its private bathroom.

Then, as we were bidding good-bye to several people, somewhat restored in spirit, a blood-curdling cry pierced the unit, followed by sobbing, screaming, and moaning that made our blood run cold. Tearing down the hall, face distorted, eyes blazing, hair disheveled, and cursing loudly was a woman we did not recognize at first as Mrs. Goodman.

"Dirty bitches, dirty bastards, they pushed me out of my room!" Her voice broke; she gasped for breath, weirdly sucked in air, and started to screech anew. The sound was so eerie I stood frozen, my astonishment even greater than my horror. This woman was a mother. Not a patient behaving in a psychotic manner . . . a mother!

She stood there distraught, panting, hurling epithets, curses, and vile oaths at everyone, the nurses and the staff, but mostly the Dalys, accusing them of plotting against her. I expected that she would turn on us next, since we and the Prouts were responsible for the change. That we were by-passed did not lessen my fear. I was terrified, speechless, and appalled by the fact that throughout all this the staff members passed blandly by, seemingly unconcerned.

"Help her," I cried, when my dry tongue could get the words out. "She's a very sick woman!" Nobody responded; with a little shrug they went on about their business. "She's a . . . a parent!" I protested, bewildered. "She's not a patient, is she? She's the parent of one." I repeated this, not intending to create panic but to enlist someone's aid in this seeming emergency.

Then suddenly I remembered the private chat we had had with the social worker the day we were being eased into the project by being briefed on other members of the group. "Mrs. Goodman is paranoiac," she'd said matter-of-factly, as if commenting on her political affiliation. That's psychiatry for you, I'd thought, throwing labels indiscriminately around, and I had dismissed it from my mind. She must have been mistaken; this project was set up for emotionally disturbed offspring, not parents.

Now all this rushed back with shocking impact. What is this, anyway? I wondered where she fit into the picture. What sort of "family" project is this? What are we getting into? I remembered, all too soon, that Linda Daly's room was on one side of ours . . . Mrs. Goodman's on the other.

My first dismay and fright had turned into indignation and apprehension so appalling that I dared not admit it to Cleve. He, too, viewed this psychotic display with amazement and concern.

We drove home in silence. There was little to say. We dared not even tell each other what we were thinking. I had an overwhelming urge to escape, to quit, to get out before it was too late. But that was preposterous. I had talked Cleve into it. The house was rented. David [their younger son] was registered in a new school. Arrangements had been made to take Ken out of the hospital. And last but far from least, Cleve was on leave from his job.

Our bridges were burned. We had to go forward . . . into what we did not know. There was no turning back now.

c. 1958

7

"Staff Has Spoken!"

WALTER FISHER, JOSEPH MEHR
AND PHILIP TRUCKENBROD

In a book about the mental health system, psychologist Walter Fisher, former assistant superintendent of Elgin State Hospital in Illinois, and two of his associates tell how an incestuous couple was committed to their hospital. All the members of the family had consented to the sexual relationship. The father and daughter were productive, working to support themselves and the mother. The staff insisted that they were dangerous to themselves and needed hospitalization.

A SOCIAL worker accidentally finds out about an incestuous situation and investigates. He discovers that a man in his sixties has been maintaining an incestuous relationship with his thirty-year-old daughter for five years. The mother, father, and daughter have agreed to the relationship. The social worker takes it upon himself to petition for the commitment of father and daughter. As a result the father loses his job and is committed; the daughter loses her job and is committed; the mother, without any means of support, goes on public aid. Eventually, the family lose their home, and the father and daughter become institutionalized. Staff has spoken!

c. 1972

38

"Admission Struggle"

A. E. HOTCHNER

Ernest Hemingway was unhappy because he couldn't concentrate on his writing. When he became suicidal, his wife and doctor convinced him to return to the psychiatric section of the Mayo Clinic in Minnesota. During an earlier stay there, Hemingway had told Hotchner that the doctors did not understand him: "What these shock doctors don't know is about writers and such things as remorse and contrition and what they do to them. They should make all psychiatrists take a course in creative writing so they'd know about writers." He said during hsi final hospitalization, "Hotch, if I can't exist on my own terms, then existence is impossible. Do you understand? That is how I've lived, and that is how I *must* live—or not live." He killed himself shortly after he left the hospital.

AT ELEVEN o'clock Sunday morning, April 23rd, I received a call from Ketchum [Idaho]. Ernest was in the Sun Valley Hospital under heavy sedation, sodium amytal every three hours, nurses around the clock.

When Mary had come into the living room that morning, she had found Ernest standing in the vestibule, where the gun rack was; he was holding a shotgun in one hand, with the breech open; he had two shells in his other hand. There was a note propped up on top of the gun rack addressed to her. Mary knew that Vernon Lord was due to come by to take Ernest's blood pressure, so she just tried to hold Ernest's attention until he got there. She knew he had been terribly depressed about his inability to write, but she had had no inkling that his depression had driven him this far.

Ernest was calm and did not make a move to put the shells in the

39

chamber, so Mary did not mention the gun at all but asked for the note. Ernest refused to give it to her but read her a few sentences here and there. There was a reference to his will and how he had provided for Mary and she wasn't to worry. Also, that he had transferred thirty thousand dollars to her checking account. Then he got off the letter and onto his latest worry, which concerned filing income taxes for the cleaning woman; talking on and on about how the Feds were sure to get him for the cleaning woman's taxes, and then Vernon arrived. When Vernon took hold of the gun Ernest let him have it without a protest.

Vernon had already put in a call to the Mayo Clinic and I was asked whether I would contact Dr. Renown and brief him on the situation.

Vernon phoned at four-thirty that afternoon. He reported that the Mayo doctors were insisting that Ernest go to Rochester voluntarily but that Ernest absolutely refused to go.

"I called Dr. Renown," I said, "and he was to call Mayo and then call you."

"He has. He made all the Mayo arrangements and discussed procedures, but I don't think he knows about this condition they've imposed, that Ernest go of his own free will. Hell, he doesn't have any *free* will! What are they talking about? I have my associate, Dr. Ausley, helping me with Ernest, but we're fighting the clock. We don't have proper facilities for this kind of thing and, Hotch, honest to God, if we don't get him to the proper place, and *fast,* he is going to kill himself for sure. It's only a question of time if he stays here, and every hour it grows more possible. He says he can't write any more— that's all he's talked to me about for weeks and weeks. Says there's nothing to live for. Hotch, he won't ever write again. He can't. He's given up. That's the motivation for doing away with himself. At least, on the surface. And that's what I have to accept because I'm not equipped to deal with anything beneath the surface. But that's strong enough motivation as far as I'm concerned, and I can tell you I'm worried sick. We've got him shot full of sodium amytal, but how long can we keep him in that state? I can tell you it's a terrible responsibility for a country doctor. It's not just that he's my friend, but he's *Ernest Hemingway.* We've *got* to get him to Mayo."

For the rest of that day we phoned back and forth between New York, Ketchum, Hollywood and Rochester, but the Mayo doctors could not be induced to come to Ketchum or vary in any way from their adamant policy that patients must enter the clinic voluntarily.

Dr. Renown suggested to Vernon Lord several procedures to be tried on Ernest to induce his co-operation. I wanted to go to Ketchum to help out, but Dr. Renown thought I should wait and go as a second echelon if Vernon failed.

The following day Mary phoned, terribly shaken. There had been a nightmarish incident. Vernon had finally gotten Ernest to consent to re-entering Mayo, and the charter plane had been summoned from Hailey. Ernest said, however, that before he went there were some things he had to get from the house. Vernon said he would send Mary for them, but Ernest said they were things he had to get himself and he would not go to Mayo without them. So Vernon reluctantly consented, but first he called Don Anderson, who is six foot three and over two hundred pounds, to come along. Vernon took the nurse and Mary also.

They drove up to the house, the five of them, and Ernest started toward the door, followed by Don, then the nurse, then Mary and Vernon. Suddenly Ernest cut loose for the door, slammed it and bolted it before Don could get there. Don raced around to the other door, charged into the house and spotted Ernest at the gun rack, holding a gun and ramming a shell into the chamber. Don hurled himself at Ernest and knocked him down. There was a terrible struggle over the gun. Vernon had to help. Luckily, the safety had been on so it did not go off. Ernest was now back at the hospital, more heavily drugged.

He was now saying he would not return to Mayo's, but Vernon was keeping the plane at the Sun Valley airstrip in the hope that he could change Ernest's mind. In the meantime, discussions were being held with people at Menninger's.

The next morning Mary phoned to say that Ernest had suddenly consented to go and the plane had just taken off for Rochester. Vernon and Don Anderson had gone with him. Mary was just barely holding herself together. She promised to have Vernon call as soon as he got back.

It was after midnight when the call came through. Vernon said that he had given Ernest a heavy sedation before taking off but that shortly after they had become airborne, Ernest had made a strenuous effort to get the door open and jump out of the plane. It had taken all of Don's and Vernon's combined strength to get him away from the door. Vernon had then given Ernest a large injection of sodium amytal, and soon thereafter he had become drowsy.

41

BLUE JOLTS

Shortly afterward the small plane had begun to develop engine trouble and had had to be landed at Casper, Wyoming. On leaving the plane, Ernest had tried to walk into a moving propeller, but Don had had him by the arm and pushed himself between Ernest and the propeller, although in so doing Ernest had almost inadvertently bumped Don into the whirling prop.

It had taken a couple of hours to repair the plane, but Ernest had seemed quiet until they were on their way again; then over South Dakota, having feigned sleep for an hour, he had made a second attempt to jump out of the plane.

Mayo doctors were waiting for them when they landed in Rochester, and Ernest, who was now docile and greeted the doctors like old friends, was immediately taken to St. Mary's, where he was placed in a special security section and put under constant surveillance.

"You know the date?" I asked.

"The twenty-fifth, isn't it?"

"Yes, almost three months to the day since they discharged him."

"Not a very long cure, was it?"

1961

9

"The Insanity Bit (I)"

SEYMOUR KRIM

Krim was taken to a mental hospital once when he was in an unihibited, free-wheeling state and again after he almost killed himself. He admits that he was immature and reckless at the time but points out that he "was aware of the 'daringness' of my every move; it represented at heart an existential *choice* rather than a mindless discharge." He experiences mental hospitals as "isolation chambers . . . a roped-off side-street of modern existence, rife with as many contradictions, half-truths and lousy architecture as life itself."

See the Release section for the second portion of Krim's narrative.

UNTIL THIS time of complete blast-off in seemingly every department of human life, the idea of insanity was thought of as the most dreadful thing that could happen to a person. Little was actually know about it and the mind conjured up pictures of Bedlam, ninnies walking around in a stupor, a living death that lasted until the poor damned soul's body expired and peace tucked him or her away for eternal keeps. But in this era of monumental need to re-think and re-define almost every former presumption about existence—which has inspired a bombing way of looking at what once were considered the most unbudgeable rocks of reality—the locked door of insanity has been shaken loose and shall yet be hurled wide open. Until one day the prisoners of this definition will walk beside us sharing only the insane plight of mortality itself, which makes quiet madmen of us all.

Every American family has its "psychotic" cousin or uncle; every friend has wept, prayed, hoped (and finally slid into indifference) for

BLUE JOLTS

another friend sweating it out in insulin or electric-shock behind the gray walls (public institution) or beyond the clipped roses (private sanitarium). Although my brother, Herbert J. Krim, was institutionalized when I was barely in my 20's—and I cosigned the certificate for a prefrontal lobotomy which ended with his death by hemorrhage on the operating table at Rockland State Hospital—I still had the conventional ideas about insanity that are shared by all "responsible" readers of *The New York Times*. It is true that as a serious writer I had inherited a great tradition of complete independence and honesty to my actual experience, regardless of what I was supposed to feel; but this was sabotaged by my youth, my ignorance, and an inability to separate my own personal life from a responsibility to question the cliches of experience to their ultimate depth. Like most American writers, from would-be's to celebrities, I was intensely preoccupied by my acutely painful and highly exaggerated subjective image—the Jewish cross, looks, sex, masculinity, a swarm of fears and devices for concealment that were secondary to my decent abilities and serious obligations as a writer intent on telling the truth. In other words: I was too narcissistically and masturbatorially stuck on myself to appreciate the horrible waste of my brother Herbert's death; and with the snotty sense of superiority usually felt by the young American writer, I thought *I* would be forever immune to the judgments of a society which I loftily ignored, or nose-thumbed, without ever coming to grips with on the actual mat of life. Like every creative type of my generation whom I met in my 20's, I was positive I was sanctified, protected by my "genius," my flair, my overwhelming ambition.

I was as wrong as you can be and still live to tell about it. In the summer of 1955, when I was 33, the thousand unacknowledged human (not literary) pressures in my being exploded. I ran barefooted in the streets, spat at members of my family, exposed myself, was almost bodily thrown out of the house of a Nobel Prize-winning author [Ernest Hemingway], and believed God had ordained me to act out every conceivable human impulse without an ounce of hypocritical caution. I know today that my instinct was sound, but my reasoning was self-deceptive. It was not God who ordained me, but I who ordained God for my own understandable human purposes. I needed an excuse to force some sort of balance between my bulging inner life and my timid outer behavior, and I chose the greatest and most comforting symbol of them all. He was my lance

44

and my shield as I tore through the New York streets acting out the bitter rot of a world-full of frustrations that my human nature could no longer lock up. I was finally cornered on the 14th floor of the St. Regis Hotel by two frightened friends and another brother; and with the aid of handcuffs seriously-humorously clipped on by a couple of bobbies I was led off to Bellevue, convinced all along that I was right. I tolerated those who took me away with the kindly condescension of a fake Jesus.

From Bellevue I was soon transferred to a private laughing academy in Westchester and given insulin-shock treatments. No deep attempt was made to diagnose my "case"—except the superficial and inaccurate judgment that I had "hallucinated." Factually, this was not true; I did not have visual images of people or objects which were not there; I merely believed, with the beautiful relief of absolute justice which the soul of man finds when life becomes unbearable, that God had given me the right and the duty to do everything openly that I had secretly fantasied for years. But this distinction was not gone into by my judges and indifferent captors. They did not have the time, the patience, or even the interest because work in a flip-factory is determined by mathematics: you must find a common denominator of categorization and treatment in order to handle the battalions of miscellaneous humanity that are marched past your desk with high trumpets blowing in their minds.

Like all the other patients, I was considered beyond reasoning with and was treated like a child; not brutally, but efficiently, firmly and patronizingly. In the eyes of this enclosed world I had relinquished my rights as an adult human being. The causes for my explosion were not even superficially examined, nor was the cheek-pinching house psychiatrist—with a fresh flower in the button hole of his fresh daily suit—truly equipped to cope with it even if he had tried, which he did not. Private sanitariums and state institutions, I realized much later, were isolation chambers rather than hospitals in the usual sense; mechanical "cures" such as the one I underwent in a setup of unchallenged authority, like the Army or a humanitarian prison, slowly brought 75 per cent of the inmates down to a more temporarily modest view of reality. Within nine or ten weeks I too came down, humbled, ashamed, willing to stand up before the class and repeat the middle-class credo of limited expressiveness and the meaning of a dollar in order to get my discharge.

In three months' time I was out, shaken, completely alone, living in a cheap Broadway hotel-room (having been ashamed to go back to Greenwich Village) and going to a conventional Ph.D. psychologist (I had been to three medically-trained therapists in the preceding decade) as a sop to both my conscience and family. I had broken beyond the bounds of "reality"—a shorthand word which is used by the average psychiatrist for want of the more truthfully complex approach that must eventually accommodate our beings' increasing flights into higher altitudes—and come back to the position I was in before. But once again the causes that had flung me into my own sky continued to eat me up. Sexually unconfident, I went to whores, ate my meals alone, and forced myself to write a few pieces in that loneliest of places, a tiny blank hotel-room in the middle of nowhere. For the first time in my life the incentive to live, the isolation and frustration of my existence, grew dim; while the psychologist smiled and smoked his pipe—and did the well-adjusted, tweedy, urbane act behind his tastefully battered desk as he ladled out platitudes—I was saving up the sleeping bombs, and when I had enough to do the trick I burned the letters I had received through the years from the several men and women I had loved, destroyed my journal of 15 years' standing, and one carefully chosen night went to a hotel in Newark, N.J.

My plan was to take the pills and slowly conk out in the full bathtub, ultimately drowning like Thomas Heggen; if one missed the other would work. I splurged on a beautiful death-room in a modernistic hotel, one that included a bathroom with the biggest tub in the house. But it was too small to fit my long body. The idea of not being able to drown and of surviving the pills afterwards, perhaps to become a burden or an invalid, began to scar what seemed like a paradise of suicide. I went instead to a Polish bar in downtown Newark, vaguely seeking the eternal anodynes of snatch and booze while I mentally played with my fate.

I found the booze and saw a coarse, ignorant Polish girl do such a life-giving, saucy, raucous folk-dance (on the small dance-floor to the right of the bar) that I broke into loving sobs like prayers over my drink. The sun of life blazed from her into my grateful heart. I went back to the beautiful hotel-room, poured the pills down the toilet, and went to sleep. The next morning I returned to Manhattan a chastened man, shaking my head at how close I had come to non-being.

When I told my tale to Mr. Pipe, my psychologist, he speedily hustled me off to a legitimate head-doctor who doped me until a private ambulance came. Very much in my right and one and only mind but too paralyzed by drugs to move, I was once again taken on the long ride—this time to another hedge-trimmed bin in Long Island. I was helpless to protest, mainly because of the shame and guilt I felt for even contemplating suicide. Obviously I was not crazy, mad, psychotic, out of my mind, schizophrenic, paranoiac. I was simply a tormented man-kid who had never steeled himself to face the facts of life—who didn't know what it meant to have principles and live by them come grief or joy—and who thought that human worth and true independence comes as easily as it does in the movies we were all emotionally faked on. As a sputtering fiction-writer and fairly active literary critic, I had had occasional peaks of maturity and illumination, but as a man I was self-deceptive, self-indulgent, crying inwardly for the pleasures of a college-boy even while in my imagination I saw myself as another Ibsen or Dreiser. Ah, the extraordinary mismating of thoughts in the mind of the modern American literary romantic, as fantastic and truly unbelievable a stew of unrelated dreams as have ever been dreamt, believe me!

Once again I was on the human assembly-line: electric shock clubbed my good brain into needless unconsciousness (and I walked to my several executions like a brave little chappie instead of questioning them) and unquestioned Old Testament authority ruled our little club. Good-natured, but mostly cowlike and uneducated male orderlies carried out the orders from above; and apart from the mechanical treatment and the unimaginative grind of occupational therapy, each patient was left completely on his or her bewildered own, a sad and farcical sight when one considered the $125 per week that their frightened families were paying.

I saw now that nine-tenths of the people I was quartered with were not "insane" by any of the standards a normally intelligent person would use: the majority had lost confidence in their own ability to survive in the world outside, or their families were *afraid* of them and had palmed them off on "experts," but positively no serious effort was being made to equip them to become free and independent adults. This was their birthright—beyond country and society, indeed an almost religious obligation—but they were palliated with pills or jolted with shock, their often honest rage echoed back to them as a sign of their "illness." Some of them must have been "sick," you say. I answer: Who can not be conceived as such in a world so complex ("The truth is there is a truth on every side"—Richard Eberhart) that each group has its own method for judging manners, behavior, ideas, and finally the worth of human values? What was more important was that I, a person from a hip milieu and with a completely opposite set of values, could see their so-called sickness with the human sensibility that an immersion in literature and experience had given me—rather than as a clinical manifestation. When I later recognized the objective provinciality of many psychiatrists in precisely the humanistic areas that could cover the actions of the majority of the inmates without finding it "psychotic," I realized that the independent thinker and artist today must learn to be resolute towards a subtle, socially powerful god-father who often drips paternalism: namely, the newly-enthroned psychiatric minority that has elevated itself to a dangerous position of "authority" in the crucial issues of mind, personality, and sanity.

I now began to fight persistently—but still with shakiness—for my release; my life was my own: it did not belong to the clichés of the salesman-aggressive, well-barbered, Jewish-refugee (my brother, my enemy!) house psychiatrist or to my smiling, betweeded nonentity of a psychologist, who paid me diplomatically inscrutable visits like a Japanese ambassador. Even if I had been or if there were such a reality as a "raving maniac"—which, perhaps childishly, I implore the over-imaginative, zeitgeist-vulnerable reader to believe is an impossible conception today—I would and should have fought for my release. What the institution-spared layman does not realize is that a sensitive and multiple-reacting human being remains the same everywhere, including a sanitarium, and such an environment can duplicate the injustice or vulgarity which drove your person there in the first place. By this I mean that a mental hospital is not an asylum or a sanctuary in the old-fashioned sense: it is just a roped-off side-street of modern existence, rife with as many contradictions, half-truths and lousy architecture as life itself.

Both of the sanitariums I was in were comparable to Grossinger's, in that they took in only financially comfortable, conventionally middle-class, non-intellectual people. By every human standard my being there was life's sarcastic answer to whatever romantic ideas I had about justice. Since the age of 19 I had deliberately led an existence of experimentation, pursuit of truth, bohemianism, and non-commercialism: fate's punishment for my green naivete was for me to recover my supposed mental health in this atmosphere of uncriticizable authority, air-conditioned by just the whiffs of truth that are perfumed and bland, and based on a pillar of middle-class propriety with the cut-throat reality of money underneath. Could I accept my former life, which had produced some good work, as a lie to myself—which the house psychiatrist wanted me to do (in effect) in his one psychotherapeutic pass at me (he left me alone after this)? I could not and never would: not only for myself but for the great principles and accomplishments of others, both living and dead, which had been my guide throughout my adult life. I might fail—but why go on having an identity at all if in a crisis you will throw away not only your past years, but the moral achievements of rare souls who have shared in your emotional and intellectual experience and whose own contributions to existence are also at stake?

When I heard this second house-psychiatrist literally equate sanity with the current cliches of adjustment and describe Greenwich Village as a "psychotic community," I saw with sudden clarity that *insanity* and *psychosis* can no longer be respected as meaningful definitions—but are used by limited individuals in positions of social power to describe ways of behaving and thinking that are alien, threatening, and *obscure* to them. (A year later when I took a psychiatrist friend of mine to the San Remo, she told me with a straight face that it reminded her of the "admission ward in Bellevue," where she had interned. This was her analogy on the basis of accurate but limited experience, that increasing chasm which separates intelligent people from understanding each other. I realized with a sense of almost incommunicable helplessness that the gap between her and the well-know poet with whom I had had a beer at the Remo two weeks before was tremendous, and that between these two poles of intelligence the neutral person—who could see the logic of each— was being mashed up with doubt and conflict. The poet was at home, or at least the heat was off, there; while the psychiatrist felt alien and had made a contemptuous psycho-sociological generalization. There was little bond of shared values and therefore genuine communication between both of these intelligent and honest human beings, each of whom contributed to my life.)

To finish with my four months in the sanitarium, I argued and reasoned for the basic right to the insecurity of freedom, and finally a good friend did the dirty in-fighting of getting me out. Had I to do it over again, I believe I would now have the guts to threaten such an institution or psychologist with a law suit, ugly as such a procedure can be to a person already vulnerable with the hash-marks of one legally defined "psychotic episode" and the contemplation of the criminal act of suicide. But I had been—as so many of Jack Kerouac's subterraneans are when faced with the machinery of offical society— milk and sawdust when, in such situations, you must be iron and stone in spite of you own frailty. It is not that the present-day authorities of mental life want to railroad anyone as in your Grade C horror movie; it is merely that as one grows older it becomes clear that there are almost irremediable differences between people in the total outlook towards life.

Mine had hardened as a result of my experiences, and I realized it was better to die out in the world if need be than be deprived of the necessity to confront existence because of the cheap authority of a lock and key. The majority of people who stay in mental institutions for any length of time do not want to return to the uncertain conditions outside the wall: which in our time spells out to emotionally anarchic, multidimensional, brain-trying, anxiety-loaded, and —O hear me mortality, from the Year One—ultimate and divine life.

1955

10

"A Sorting Problem"

SERGEANT ALBERT SYKORA

In telling about bringing people to local mental hospitals, Sergeant Sykora of the Cicero, Illinois, Police Department hits on the key question: "Is a law being broken?"

WHEN SOMEONE turns to the police for help, his attitude is often that of turning to his last resort. Other efforts have failed and finally the police are brought into the picture. People who make such a choice are usually desperate. Recently a woman who had gone for days without sleep turned to the police for help. She had been kept awake by her husband who had been beating her and threatening her life. Finally she came to the station and signed a complaint on a minor charge and he was arrested. The next day he was taken to a psychiatrist for examination and found to be in need of treatment.

The sad thing about this case was the wife's reluctance to sign charges against her husband. She did not want to be caught in the middle between him and the law. Moreover, she did not want to have to face him upon his release. Such a predicament often leads to pressuring the police to act without the person himself becoming openly involved.

In less serious situations, usually during a long weekend when the husband and wife spend a lot of time together, the police are often called to break up a quarrel and to lock up one of the mates. By the next morning everyone cools off and charges are dropped.

The point of the above is that the police see people in settings not often encountered by many mental health professionals. They are seen in the home, the squadrol, jail and at hospital intake. In each instance they appear in their most upset condition, and because of this they are also among the most difficult to manage.

In bringing people to the hospital we try to use as little force as possible. Usually we try to talk to them in a calm, familiar way, telling them they are going to see the doctor at the hospital.

When we bring someone into the hospital we are faced with several problems. Upon bringing a person to the hospital we often find that when he gets there he refuses to sign a voluntary admission form and runs away. Also, even when he is kept for evaluation or other reasons, he may be released shortly after we leave the hospital. A few hours later we are again faced with bringing in the same person. This seems to happen more frequently during the evening hours. The hospitals' discharge policies are confusing to us.

While waiting to be seen at intake with a patient, sometimes for over an hour, we are often called upon to restrain the patient. Even with the best conditions, such tasks are often upsetting to others watching in the waiting room. The public has not seen prior management problems the police have had in bringing the person to the hospital and do not realize the possible trouble which would occur if the police did not use enough force to restrain the person. We are then seen as being unjustly forceful. A special waiting area for police would be appreciated.

Another set of problems arise when we are summoned to the house where the caller is either using us or does not know what is wrong but wants us to make a decision. For example, we are sometimes called on to remove someone from the home merely because someone else is angry with them, not because a law has been broken. A similarly confusing problem occurs when someone exhibits some sort of temper tantrum, seizure or other puzzling behavior. In these cases we are faced with a sorting problem. Are such people physically ill, mentally ill, or malingering?

To be sure, there are still problems in the community mental health system; however, things have gotten better since the inception of catchment areas. A few years back the police had no definite single place to bring people and often ended up taking people from one hospital to another before we found a place that would accept them.

c. 1973

"The Start of the Way of the Cross"

VALERY TARSIS

Because Tarsis's *The Bluebottle* (1962) was critical of the Khrushchev regime, he was sent to Moscow's Kashchenko mental hospital for seven months. Through Valentine Almazov, the protagonist in his fictionalized autobiography, *Ward 7,* expatriate Tarasis recounts his examination at a way station for inmates, and his ambulance ride and admission to Kaschenko mental hospital, which he nicknames Kanatchikov Villa.

In striking parallel to the Chekhov passage that Tarsis quotes at the beginning of his selection, Sovietologist Peter Reddaway reports what a psychiatrist said to Soviet dissident Vladimir Borisov's wife when she protested that her husband was sane. The doctor replied, "Maybe, but he was unlucky; he is down on our register. What may be a system of opinions in a normal person is a sign of illness in your husband."

"BUT THERE are hundreds of lunatics who are at large, just because you are too ignorant to recognise they are insane. Why should I and these other wretches have to sit here instead of them and be your scapegoats? Morally, you and your assistant and the other scoundrels on your staff are infinitely worse than we are—why are we locked up and not you? Where's the logic of it?"

"Neither logic nor morality have anything to do with it. It's a matter of luck. If you've been locked up you are inside, if you haven't you are

53

> free. That's all there is to it. The fact that you
> are a mental patient or that I am a doctor is
> purely a matter of chance."
>
> Anton Chekov
> *Ward 6*

In the morning Almazov was examined by the head city psychiatrist, exactly as a prisoner is examined by a magistrate. He was brought to Dr. Yanushkevich's consulting room under guard. The doctor made no attempt to treat him as a patient; illness was never even mentioned. Pink and smug, he seemed to take his role as prosecutor for granted. Valentine, now that he had got through the night, was calmer and ready to face his way of the cross.

"What's the game, eh?—writing anti-Soviet letters to foreign embassies?"

"Are you in the police? I thought that doctors at least were exempt."

"That's no way to talk."

"I don't wish to talk to a policeman."

"You are wasting my time. They can sort you out at Kanatchikov's." He called the guard. "Take him back."

"You are a poor interrogator, you haven't learned your job yet," Valentine put in as a parting shaft.

It was raining. The same woman doctor, who had been on duty the night before, saw him to the ambulance. He was driven away under the triple escort of another doctor and two medical students, part of whose training consisted in acting as guards. One of them asked him if he was quite comfortable.

Almazov was preoccupied with the notion, still new to him but for which he was finding more and more corroborating evidence—that, so far from being socialist, the system which had finally become established in Russia was a particularly vicious form of fascism.

"You remind me," he replied indifferently, "of the executioner who asks his victim: 'May I trouble you?'"

The students exchanged glances but said nothing. As Valentine was to discover later, mental patients had one important privilege. On condition that they remained calm (if they became violent they were given an injection), they could say whatever they chose and the staff were not allowed to answer back.

An hour after he arrived he was interviewed by the doctor in charge, Lydia Kizyak, who was the medical head of the section. Valentine immediately sensed in her the inhuman bureaucratic type usually admired as "one hundred per cent Soviet." There was a silence while they looked at each other as warily as two duellists.

Born in 1917, Lydia Kizyak was a worthy contemporary of the Revolution. Having made her career by hook or crook, she clung to her position and was terrified of losing it.

She loved power, it was her only passion; yet she was nervous as a cat.

"Well, let's get on with it," she began briskly. "Tell me about your illness, your family, your background . . ."

I forbid you to play the fool with me," Almazov said with deliberation. "I don't suppose you want a row, so we'd better agree on our terms of reference."

She fidgeted in her chair and looked round anxiously. There was no one else in the large interview room, but just then an orderly came in with a paper for her to sign. She signed it hastily and told him to deliver it and come straight back. Almazov gave her a withering glance.

"This is the position. I don't regard you as a doctor. You call this a hospital, I call it a prison to which, in a typically fascist way, I have been sent without trial. So now, let's get everything straight. I am your prisoner, you are my jailer, and there isn't going to be any nonsense about my health or my relations, or about examination or treatment. Is that understood?"

"We'll have to use compulsory methods."

"You can try."

"All right. We'll see."

1963

12

"Kavka and Pound"

CHARLES OLSON

During World War II, Ezra Pound made over three hundred radio broadcasts from Italy in which he attacked the United States and "the world conspiracy of Jewish bankers," assisting propaganda campaigns conducted for Radio Roma. Near the end of the war he gave himself up to the invading Americans, who placed him in a special cage made of airstrip steel in the yard of the detention camp at Pisa. After a few weeks of exposure to heat, dust, and moisture, Pound had hysterical fits of terror, and the prison doctor moved him to a tent in the medical compound. When Pound was brought back to the United States to stand trial for treason, lawyer Julian Cornell argued that the poet needed mental hospital treatment because of his experience at Pisa. Cornell was actually trying to get Pound out of the Washington, D.C., jail without risking denial of bail. He was also trying to delay the treason trial so that the public pressure for severity might abate. The court remanded Pound to Gallinger Hospital for "examination and observation."

The three government psychiatrists and one defense-appointed psychiatrist who examined Pound at Gallinger concluded that he was "paranoid" and legally insane and as such not capable of consulting with counsel in his defense. They added that Pound was "in need of care in a mental hospital." The prosecution, though, suspected that Pound was feigning insanity—in Nuremberg only three weeks earlier Rudolf Hess had confessed to feigning amnesia—and pressed for a jury trial on Pound's mental state. Pound was duly transferred to Saint Elizabeths Hospital, a federal mental hospital in a suburb of Washington, where he was consigned to the prison ward, maximum security Howard Hall. A Dr. Jerome Kavka was in attendance.

At the insanity trial Superintendent Winfred Overholser of Saint Elizabeths, the star government psychiatric examiner and witness,

56

was so zealous that he purposely did not reveal to the court that the junior doctors at Saint Elizabeths thought Pound merely eccentric— and wanted him tried and convicted. Also, Overholser had convinced the three other examining psychiatrists that they should submit a unanimous report, lest the jury have a real say in deciding the issue. His strategy worked. In the face of psychiatric unanimity, Judge Bolitha Laws and the prosecution and defense lawyers decided during a brief conference at the bench not to call Pound as a witness. The judge instructed the jury to bear strongly in the mind "unequivocal view" of the medical witnesses and weakly allowed that the jurors were not absolutely bound by the expert testimony. The jury returned a verdict of insanity after five minutes' deliberation.

Pound was sent back to Saint Elizabeths until such time as he would be fit to stand trial. His lawyer soon convinced Overholser to transfer Pound from the prison ward to the Chestnut Ward. Since Pound was supposedly incurably insane, unable to stand trial, and according to the doctors not dangerous, his lawyer argued that the poet should be released. He was refused. In 1958 poet Robert Frost helped untangle the knot by appealing to presidential assistant Sherman Adams and Attorney General William Rogers, and retaining lawyer Thurman Arnold. Superintendent Overholser still held that Pound was "permanently and incurably insane," but agreed that he was not dangerous. He belatedly admitted that "confinement can serve no therapeutic purpose." Judge Laws then dismissed the indictment and Pound went free.

In this selection, poet-Charles Olson recalls a visit with Pound shortly after he entered Saint Elizabeths. Pound complains about the medical cross-examination by resident psychiatrist Kavka. He goes on to give an example of his own medical scientism in the form of a scurrilous attack on Jews. Olson reacts by thinking Pound a "fascist bastard," but persists in the notion that Pound is "sick." The selection illustrates some absurdities of hospitalization: Pound is placed in a mental hospital instead of being tried for treason; Kavka persists in analyzing Pound's mental state; Olson considers his colleague sick; and Pound himself makes an attack on spurious medical grounds.

In 1956, toward the end of his hospital stay, Pound wrote with some acuity: "Psychotherapical institutions, so far as is ascertainable, are run on the supposition that nobody has any nerves, nobody has any perceptions, and that none of the patients perserves any trace of logical faculty, not necessarily for syllogisms and trains of thought, but for immediate perception of cause and effect."[1] In what stands as an ironic rejoinder, Kavka wrote in 1975, "Post-therapeutic confessionals, written under intense abreactive pressure and unneutralized exhibitionism, often betray their underlying motives of subtle revenge towards the disappointing treatment."[2]

IN POUND I am confronted by the tragic Double of our day. He is the demonstration of our duality. In language and form he is as forward, as much the revolutionist as Lenin. But in social, economic and political action he is as retrogressive as the Czar.

And then Pound jumped ahead to 1914 and Poland, and something about they were wise enough to get out. Or he was, I couldn't quite get it clear. (This date seemed to be important, for Pound there took a swing at the doctor Kavka, whom, he said, thinks that all my trouble starts there, 1914, Poland.)*

I believe it was here too that Pound said, "I told Potocki,† is that how you pronounce it? I said, Potostcki, and he went on,"I told him not to trust England." (Familiar?)

Pound's complaint about the doctor served somehow to create the gayety of the meeting, despite the anti-semitism which mixed itself into it. For poor Kavka does seem to be scared to death of this Pound business, and to be handling it in an absurd way because of his fear and uncertainty. God knows it is causing Pound a good deal of what I'm sure is unnecessary pain. He says Kavka keeps pounding questions at him . . . . and punched his fist against the wall of his other hand to illustrate the effect. He says he wakes up the following morning exhausted from trying to think back and work out the answers to his questions.

I tried to get him to take Kavka less seriously, telling Pound K is frightened to death, not of him as so much, as of the fact it is the Ezra

---

*Dr. Jerome Kavka does not recall any particular reference to Poland by Pound except in reference to Kavka's Polish origins on those occasions when Pound felt a need to strike back at his questioner. Kavka does believe that Pound's bitterness over the outbreak of World War I in 1914 and the resulting deaths of Gaudier and Hulme had much to do with his later problems. (Conversation between Dr. Kavka and Catherine Seelye, December 28, 1973.)

†Count Jerzy Potocki (1889-1961), Polish ambassador to the United States, 1936-1940. Pound lunched with Potocki while in Washington in 1939.

Pound case. And that he's no more than a graduate student, trying to act professional.

At this Pound says, I never knew a doctor less scientific. If they want to examine me, why don't they give me some scientist, I wouldn't mind. He merely acts like a goddamn bureaucrat. But this intolerable questioning. Good god, what the hell, what the hell difference does it make what I was reading in 1902! (At this point Pound just continued to swear, and wondering if there was any "lady" in the next cubicle, saying he wouldn't want to shock them, he jumps up and looks around the corner, and finding none, continues to let it rip.

"With ANTISEMITE spread all over the front page of PM, you can't expect much else," he said, alluding to K, who was born Jonah Kafka, and is now Jerome Kavka,* as he told me when I gave him Pound's *Kulch and Cantos—*. (At that time K said, it hadn't made any impression on EP when he had learned his name was Kafka.)

Pound then followed up, "The other doctor I didn't mind." He meant Tiny, who had been in charge that one Sunday CC had visited. Tiny Ziman.† I pointed out to Pound that Tiny used to be a master of ceremonies in a night club, and had some experience with people. But that K was just a kid. Told him I had tried to get Tiny to bring K and me together informally.†† And would try again. But that K has so far backed away from me. Probably K is also scared of that s.o.b. Griffin,§ who is his boss.

Pound said, "They (meaning jews) were nice to me at the DDC** (jail?)."

"I guess the definition of a lunatic is a man surrounded by them."

He was quiet for a minute, working his forehead, when he started out, talking down and away toward the window to his right and my left: "There was a Jew, in London, Obermeyer, a doctor of comparative . . . . . of the endocrines, and I used to ask him what is

---

*Max Brod, in *Franz Kafka; Eine Biographie,* points out that Kavka is the correct spelling of this name.

†Dr. Edmund Ziman "was called Tiny because he was a very portly man resembling to some extent one of his close personal friends, Zero Mostel. He had a great sense of humor and was most articulate." Letter to Catherine Seelye from Jerome Kavka, August 21, 1973.

††Olson invited Kavka to dinner on January 4, 1946 (the day of Olson's first visit to Pound). Kavka declined "for fear of compromising the case." Ibid.

§Dr. Edgar D. Griffin, Clinical Director of Clinical Branch II, St. Elizabeths Hospital.

**DTC. Disciplinary Training Center, Mediterranean Theater of Operations USA, near Pisa.

the effect of circumcision. That's the question that gets them sore," and he begins to be impish as hell, "that sends them right up the pole. Try it, don't take my word, try it." And then, with a pitiful seriousness, turning directly toward me and says: "It must do something, after all these years and years, where the most sensitive nerves in the body are, rubbing them off, over and over." (It was fantastic, again the fascist bastard, the same god damned kind of medical nonsense Hitler and the gang used with the same seriousness, the same sick conviction.) It was so cockeyed for the moment it was funny actually, absurd, and I was carried along by this swearing, swift, slashing creature.

I record it, but here as elsewhere, it is impossible to give a true impression. For at any given point, always, there is the presence of the seriousness of the man. Even in his sickest and most evil moments. He is always a man at work, examining, examining. Here, for example, on the one hand he is attacking K as a Jew, when the truth is K is making the mistakes of any young man, and Pound is god damned well lucky it is K and not the monster Griffin who is questioning him, is in charge. I could not help feeling during this whole line of Pound's, how it was precisely the Jews around him here and in the DDC* who gave him some warmth and help, how it was through Tiny and K that I had got drawers issued to him, how it was K who at least had the curiosity to read his verse, and that K, in Chicago, when the bookstores said, they wouldn't carry the books of a fascist, objected and damn well told them that was the same as burning books, and plain out and out fascist.

1946

---

*Ibid.

13

"A Need to Disrupt the Lives of Others"

ROBERT COLES

When Reverend Herbert Callender tried to put Mayor Wagner of New York City under citizen's arrest for permitting racial bias in the construction of city housing projects, Callender was arrested and sent to Bellevue Hospital for "mental observation" (*The New York Times,* July, 16, 1964, page 12).

Psychiatrist Robert Coles presents a similar case. He heard a southern judge send a young black civil rights activist to a state mental hospital for observation and evaluation of "possible delinquent and sociopathic trends." The victim describes his treatment, and Dr. Coles comments on the episode.

"IT'S QUITE a setup they've got. We protest our inability to vote, to go into a movie or restaurant everyone else uses, and they call us crazy, and send us away to be looked over by psychiatrists and psychologists and social workers and all the rest of them. The questions I've had put at me since I've been here! Were you a *loner* when you were a boy? Did people consider you *rebellious?* Were you *popular* or *unpopular* as a child? When you were younger did you have trouble *taking orders* from your parents or your teachers? Did your mother *discipline* you firmly, or did she more or less let you do as you please? And on and on they go, one question after another, and none of them very subtle.

"The guy doing the questioning told me he is a doctor, a psychiatrist, and I asked him why he wasn't interested in *what* I've done, and the *objective reasons* I've acted as I have. But he said he

61

BLUE JOLTS

knew 'all that.' He told me his job is to examine my mind and find out
what my 'motivations' are. He kept on asking me whether I feel angry
at this person and that one, and if I have a temper, and how do I
'handle tension,' and he wanted to know whether people in 'authority'
make me anxious, and whether I have trouble in 'controlling' myself,
and whether I 'rush out and act' when I come upon an unpleasant
situation, or instead do I stop and think and try to figure out the best
possible 'attitude' to have. I wrote them down, as many of his words
and questions as I could, because the way he put those questions was
to me more abusive than anything I've ever heard from the poor,
ignorant rednecks. At least they have the decency to insult you right
to your face; so you know exactly where they stand and no one's
fooling anyone, least of all himself. That doctor (I can tell from
talking with him over a week) considers himself way above the red-
neck; in his mind he is a careful, thoughtful, temperate man. He used
that word 'temperate' two or three times with me. He kept on
contrasting 'temperate behavior' with 'impulsive behavior,' and after
we got talking more casually he told me that some people have a
'need'—that's right, a *need*—to disrupt the lives of others, and hurt
them, and get hurt themselves. Did I think I was that kind of person?

"Soon you just slip into the whole scene. I mean, you stop noticing
all the assumptions a guy like that constantly makes, and you simply
try to answer him as best you can. And anyway, if you protest and tell
him off, tell him what you think is implicit in his questions and his
whole way of thinking, he's not going to take your argument
seriously; he's going to go after *you*—and call you 'hostile' and
'defensive' and full of 'problems' and all the rest. He as much as told
me so, that doctor did. He said a lot was going on inside my mind, and
until I found out what 'really' was prompting some of my 'behavior,'
I'd probably continue what I've been doing. He told me he was going
to recommend to the court that I not be sent to jail. He said I needed
treatment—but he was worried that I would be 'resistant' to it, and
that would be 'too bad' for me, and later I would be sorry."

The youth then pointed out to me [Robert Coles] what I hope is
obvious: the smug, self-righteous arrogance he had met up with, the
pejorative use of psychiatric terminology, the limitless display of self-
satisfaction and condescension, the essentially illogical and
totalitarian nature of a mode of thought that claims to have the
authority to decide who has a right even to discuss certain matters,

62

and who (whatever he *thinks* he is saying or doing or trying to say or trying to do) is *really* "sick" or "resistant" or seriously in need of "help," and therefore thoroughly, hopelessly suspect. I was prepared to accept much of that from him—I had heard patients endlessly labeled in ways that robbed them of their dignity, and I had seen in myself as a psychiatric resident the awful tendency to dismiss a patient's disagreement or criticism as evidence of just about anything but his or her good judgment. But I was not so prepared to see how convenient it could be for that judge, and many like him, to have people around who would summon all the authority of medicine and science to the task of defending the status quo—which meant putting firmly in their place (a hospital or a clinic) those who choose to wage a struggle against that status quo.

1963

14

"Force and Fraud"

JEFFREY R. SOLOMON

In the course of an absurd series of mix-ups and delays, a suicidal woman becomes so angry that her depression subsides.

CONCERN FOR the rights of the mentally ill has often taken the form of social and legal action to release patients from mental hospitals. In fact, the community mental health center movement is based on this idea. However, prejudice against inpatient care and the limited supply of hospital beds have distorted diagnosis and treatment. In some communities it seems impossible to hospitalize a person unless he tries to kill himself or another person in front of a worker at the local receiving hospital.

Clearly it is time to extend the rights of the mentally ill to include the right to hospitalization for psychiatric problems for those who need it. Although the mental health professions have rightly been opposed to long-term hospitalization as a custodial mechanism— rather than a treatment modality—they must not abandon the whole idea of hospitalization.

The following account of an attempt to get one patient admitted to a mental hospital illustrates the insanity in the mental health system. This incident, which is typical, took place in a ten-hour period between 4 P.M. and 2 A.M. one weekday night in 1974 in a metropolitan community of 1.2 million persons.

At 4 P.M. on Monday, Mrs. P called her caseworker, Mrs. L, at the family service agency. She said she was depressed, had attempted suicide three days earlier by taking barbiturates and alcohol, and saw no reason to continue living. Mrs. L consulted with the agency administrator, Mr. J, and then called a local private hospital that provides psychiatric care to confirm that a bed was available.

When Mrs. L arrived at Mrs. P's home, all the burners of the gas stove were on and the windows were closed. She was greeted by a slap across the face from Mrs. P followed by an embrace. It took five hours to convince this acutely suicidal woman that, because no family or friends were available to care for her, hospitalization was the necessary form of treatment. Mrs. P finally agreed to hospitalization, and with additional intervention by Mr. J, Mrs. L and Mrs. P went to the hospital. Mr. J kept in touch with Mrs. L and supported her efforts. After arranging for return transportation for Mrs. L, he left for the hospital.

When Mr. J arrived at the hospital, Mrs. L informed him that no beds were available, despite information to the contrary twenty minutes earlier. He met with the resident psychiatrist who confirmed that no beds were available and stated he believed Mrs. P definitely required hospitalization because of the severity of her depression.

The director of social services, who was still at the hospital, explained that the available beds had been taken by three unexpected patients who had just been readmitted. She said that the only hope of hospitalization was at the county hospital, which has both a crisis intervention facility and an inpatient psychiatric institute. The other private psychiatric hospital in the community was filled.

Mrs. P refused to go to the county hospital because she had had a previous bad experience there. In an attempt to persuade her, Mr. J and Mrs. L enlisted the aid of a private psychiatrist affiliated with the hospital who agreed to talk with her. During the discussion between Mr. J, Mrs. L, and the psychiatrist, it was obvious that the psychiatrist thought Mrs. L was the patient. When this misunderstanding was corrected, a hospital aide tried to lock the three in the interviewing area.

The consultation and second psychiatric interview were unsuccessful. Mrs. P still reufsed to go to the county hospital voluntarily. The psychiatrist advised Mrs. L that Mrs. P would have to be an involuntary admission and should be told that she would be taken to the county hospital by the police if she continued to refuse. When Mrs. P refused again, Mrs. L called the police.

However, an involuntary admission can be arranged on the basis of an ex parte order only during the day. At night two physicians must sign a person into the hospital on an involuntary basis. It was then that Mrs. L and Mr. J came up against "Catch 22"—the two physicians who were willing to sign Mrs. P in did not have a bed for her.

Although the police are not required to help transfer a patient to a receiving facility, it was fortunate that three policemen were already at the hospital with a patient they had apprehended on an ex parte order. After Mr. J and Mrs. L pleaded with them, the police sergeant agreed to take Mrs. P to the county hospital emergency room, ten blocks away. A resident in psychiatry who knew someone at the county hospital discovered that a staff bed was available and reserved it for Mrs. P. The instructions were to go to the emergency room and tell the admitting nurse the staff bed was reserved.

The policemen forcibly took Mrs. P to the emergency room. They were not permitted to stay with her because they had no order from the court and had to return to their prisoner at the private hospital. After a thirty-minute wait in the emergency room, where there were a variety of incidents including a woman trying to defecate into the water fountain, Mr. J and Mrs. L were told that the psychiatric staff could not do an intake on Mrs. P for over one hour until the crisis clinic had closed. They were also told that no one knew anything about a bed and that they should wait and be patient. Needless to say, Mrs. P was quite agitated. However, signs everywhere indicated "We Care."

Mr. J called the administrative nurse at the psychiatric clinic and discovered that she knew of a waiting bed. She gave him directions for walking through the labyrinth of halls, including an open surgical area, to get to the crisis intervention center. On a bulletin board in the waiting room, in full view of the public, was a list of the names and appointment dates of patients as well as three memoranda listing patients who were in an antipsychotic medication research project and instructions to staff about these patients—an appalling violation of patients' rights to confidentiality.

Mrs. P would not cooperate at all during the intake interview with the social worker. The social worker then interviewed our counselor and concluded that Mrs. P might be able to have a psychiatric interview. While waiting for the psychiatrist, the counselor was asked to respond to a long research schedule on behalf of Mrs. P. The schedule had nothing to do with the evaluation, diagnosis, or treatment of Mrs. P. While waiting for the psychiatrist, Mr. J and Mrs. L also discovered that although a bed was arranged for through the clinic, no one had notified the floor and the bed had been given away.

After a ten-minute psychiatric evaluation, the psychiatrist said he did not believe that Mrs. P was a serious case. He thought her anger had been sufficiently elevated to decrease her acute depression and that she could go home, even though there were no supports for her. Mr. J and Mrs. L were able to convince him that Mrs. P did indeed need to be hospitalized. Of course, a potential patient rarely has knowledgeable professionals to serve as advocates in the intake process.

At 1:00 A.M. two male psychiatric aides came to take Mrs. P to the psychiatric floor, along with a man in his underwear who had been brought in by the police and one other admission. Mrs. P refused to go and the aides were ready to put her in restraints. At first she said, "I don't want to go with that guy in his underpants." She finally said, "Oh, what the hell!" and left with the aides. After a painful night of hospitalization and confirmation of her need for continued hospitalization by three psychiatrists, she was released the next morning. Before leaving the hospital, she called Mrs. L and said: "When I get out of here and I get depressed, I am going to kill myself. There's no help for me."

One can only conclude that the insanity of the system results indeed in lowering the acute suicidal tendency. That is, in trying simply to get admitted to the hospital, Mrs. P's anger was so aroused that it lowered her depression. However, one cannot but believe that there is a great need to reevaluate the way mental health services are provided. At the planning level, mental health professionals must look at how the mental health system works, and more important, at how it does not work. Resources have to be developed to meet those in a crisis. One knows of many cases in which a person has an electrocardiogram during a routine medical examination and the next day dies of a heart attack. Clearly, the heart attack was not preventable. However, there are too many cases of people walking into crisis centers, being given a couple of pills, walking out, and killing themselves or someone else.

From the client's point of view, mental illness should not have to beget more mental illness. As Mrs. P said as she walked through the open surgical area: "I knew that if I was taken here, I would go crazy." Surrounded, quite literally, by blood and guts, how can a depressed person not feel this way?

Within the political perspective, those responsible for health care must be made truly responsible. The center at the county facility seemed more interested in its research protocol than in meeting the client's needs. This level of care cannot be tolerated by a citizenry responsible for a public institution.

Thus the implications of this experience are clear. Mental health professionals must take a closer look at resources to insure their adequacy. However, in the short run, they must look at practices and procedures with an eye to their impact on the users of service. Delusional psychosis on the part of those responsible for the maladministration of mental health services is not a permissible defense.

1974

15

"Too Mentally Ill"

LAWRENCE AL SIEBERT

Having taken his doctorate at the University of Michigan, psychologist Siebert went to the Menninger Foundation mental hospital under a fellowship. In his third-person account, Siebert writes: "He discovered why it is that a person going into 'psychotherapy' reduces his chances of getting better and, at the request of the Menninger staff, tried to share his insights with them. Four days later he found himself locked into the back ward of the local Veterans Administration hospital. He was forced to take mind-dulling drugs and the word was spread that he had become severely mentally ill." Though loaded with Thorazine, Siebert soon "escaped."

Here he tells about the deceit that some staff members practice when it is time for the inmate to go for a court hearing.

IN SOME psychiatric observation wards a person is not told he is being committed until shortly before the time of his hearing. And then he may only find out when he is called to the ward office and told to sign a form which states that he knows about the hearing but does not wish to attend. If he asks why the hearing is being held he is likely to be told that the treatment he needs takes many months, is very expensive, and that the hearing is merely a legal formality which must be gone through in order to make the state (or federal) government pay his total hospitalization costs.

It is rarely suggested to a person that he can be present at his hearing if he wishes. If he asks to attend he may be told: it is such a routine thing it isn't worth the trip (one court has been found to

69

average 1.6 minutes per hearing); the ward is short of help and cannot release an attendant to take him; the psychistrist is too busy to go and make a full presentation of his case; or, it would be best for him to enter his treatment showing a willingness to cooperate.

If, on the other hand, a judge asks why the person isn't present, the judge hears a different story. Typical ones are: the patient desires commitment and does not want to appear; the patient is so mentally ill he would not understand what is happening; the patient is so heavily drugged it would be harmful for him to be moved; the patient is so disturbed and potentially violent he cannot be safely brought to court; or the experience of hearing the psychiatric testimony would cause the patient to become even more mentally ill.

1965

16

"Advantage of Force"

ANTONIN ARTAUD

Artaud had undergone treatment for drug addiction in Switzerland in 1936. A year later, after he created a ruckus by seeking refuge in a Jesuit college in Ireland, he was sent back to France "in a state of high exaltation." Aboard ship, he responded with a menacing gesture to two crew members who rudely entered his cabin, and the ensuing fight culminated in his arrest. Because of the Irish incident and the shipboard tumult, the authorities at the port of Le Havre had him certified insane and committed to a mental hospital.

For nine years Artaud was confined in institutions, including Villa-Evrard from 1939 to 1943, where he became delirious in a ward for drug addicts; and Rodez from 1943 to 1946, where he was given electroshock. His friends managed to have him released in 1946, but, thinking he needed watching, they sent him to the mental hospital at Ivry. There he died of cancer in 1948.

In "The Patients and the Doctors," Artaud protests, ". . . I consider/that it's up to the everlastingly sick me/to cure all doctors/—born doctors by lack of sickness—/and not up to the doctors ignorant of my dreadful/states of sickness/to impose their insulintherapy on me,/their health for a worn out world." In the powerful open letter to mental hospital superintendents that follows, he disputes the concept of mental illness and decries doctors' alienation from their captives.

LETTER TO THE MEDICAL DIRECTORS
OF LUNATIC ASYLUMS

GENTLEMEN,

Law and Custom allow you the right to evaluate human minds. You are supposed to exercise this sovereign, redoubtable jurisdiction with discernment. You won't mind if we laugh. The credulity of civilised peoples, scholars and administrators, endows psychiatry with limitless supernatural wisdom. Your profession's case is awarded the verdict in advance. We have no intention of discussing the validity of your science here, nor the doubtful existence of mental sickness. But for a hundred pretentious pathogenic diagnoses, in which confusion between mind and matter runs wild, for a hundred classifications only the vaguest of which are still any use, how many noble attempts have been made to approach the world of the mind, in which so many of your prisoners live? For instance, for how many of you are a schizophrenic's dreams and the images which haunt him anything more than a jumble of words?

We are not surprised to find you unequal to a task for which few are preordained. But we vigorously protest against the right attributed to certain men, narrowminded or not, to sanction their investigations into the domain of the mind with sentences of life imprisonment.

And what imprisonment! We all know—no, it is not widely enough known—that asylums, far from being *asylums,* are fearful jails, where the inmates provide a source of free and useful manpower and where brutality is the rule, all of which you tolerate. A mental asylum, under cover of science and justice, is comparable to a barracks, a prison or a slave colony.

We will not raise the question of arbitrary confinement. This will save you the trouble of making hasty denials. But we categorically state that a great number of your inmates, quite mad by official definition, are also arbitrarily confined. We protest against any interference with the free development of delirium. It is as legitimate, as logical as any other sequence of human ideas or acts. The repression of anti-social reactions is as chimerical as it is unacceptable in principle. All individual acts are anti-social. Madmen, above all, are individual victims of social dictatorship. In the name of individuality which specifically belongs to man, we demand the liberation of these people convicted of sensibility. For we tell you no laws are powerful enough to lock up all men who think and act.

Without stressing the perfectly inspired nature of the manifestations of certain madmen, in so far as we are capable of appreciating them, we simply affirm that their concept of reality is absolutely legitimate, as are all the acts resulting from it.

Try and remember *that* tomorrow morning during your rounds,

72

when, without knowing their language, you attempt to converse with these people over whom, you must admit, you have only one advantage, namely force.

1937-1948

II

Treatment

Introduction

One of the most salient characteristics of
the great majority of patients now in state
hospitals is that they should not have been
admitted in the first place.

Franklin Chu and Sharland Trotter
The Madness Establishment

Most large institutions are not really
treatment institutions but instead function
as custodial institutions whose primary
mission is to contain those who violate
others' sense of decency or reality.

Richard Price and Bruce Denner, editors
The Making of a Mental Patient

It is safe to say that none of us is too
satisfied with what has been accomplished
to date. We appreciate that none of our
vaunted discoveries has given us the lasting
results we desire for our patients.

Alexander Gralnick, Medical Director
High Point Hospital
*The Psychiatric Hospital
as a Therapeutic Instrument*

William Weitz became a patient on a psychiatric ward
in order to add a new dimension to his graduate
studies in psychology. He soon came to feel a strong sympathy for the
inmates' position, and, because he so identified with them, he conveys

a compelling picture of ward life in "Anger, Loneliness, Detachment, and Boredom." The opposite of his compassion is conspicuous in Dr. Lloyd Cotter's self-satisfied account of shocking and starving Vietnamese mental patients into submission, "Alleviating Schizophrenic Thinking." The ultimate in cruel, objectifying hospital treatment is seen in Soviet dissenter Leonid Plyushch's terrible sufferings, which he depicts in "Ideological Treatment." The use of behavioral conditioning in these instances suggests that conditioning techniques are not merely subject to abuse, but that in the mental hospital setting they tend to be coercive. For example, the behavioral technique known as the token economy reinforces inmates with tokens redeemable for food and other "rewards" if they cooperate and withholds tokens if they resist. Insofar as food is withdrawn to coerce and punish, the token economy resembles bygone tyrannies: "An earlier method of punishment was the 'hunger cure' used in insane asylums. Suspension in baskets over the dining table was supposed to bring people back to reason."[1] Psychiatrist E. Fuller Torrey frankly states, "Conditioning and behavior techniques . . . are about as new as the concept of a spanking."[2]

The most dramatic technique of controlling inmates that masquerades as modern scientific therapy is shock treatment. Writes Jay Haley, "In more modern and progressive mental hospitals the aides are not allowed to beat up on the patients. It is necessary for the aide to report that the patient cannot control his hostility so that the doctor can bang the patient in the head with a shock machine. This procedure maintains the proprieties for medical investigating boards who know treatment when they see it."[3] Neurologist John Friedberg echoes Haley, calling shock "just another variant of the age-old tendency for people to bop one another over the head."[4] In order to deceive the victim, and to avoid resistance, the doctor sometimes hides the shock box from the subject before he anesthetizes him.[56] Sociologist Ivan Belknap enlarges on these themes in "Worry Warts," a description of hospital employees' use of shock to control uncooperative inmates.

Electric shock is still widely employed in mental hospitals.[7] The official rationale for this "treatment" is its reorienting effect, which, when it occurs, is usually only temporary—and is generally offset by accompanying confusion and memory loss, movingly described by Reverend West in "Sixty Comas." As Dr. Herbert Walker states, electric shock rarely has positive results: "The case of electroshock is too often a case of the patient receiving unnecessary treatment, and philosophically this makes the patient a victim. . . . The recurrence rate for electroshock patients is quite high, so if shock treatment is, as some claim, beneficial, why isn't the effect lasting? Why do ECT patients exhibit a high rate of rehospitalization?"[8] The shock doctor ignores the ineffectiveness of treatment and blithely dismisses the side effects—unless he has special reason to esteem the inmate: "The decision to use electroconvulsive therapy as a treatment for physician-patient was approached with great caution. As a group, physicians place great stress on their mental prowess, and consequently the transient confusion of mentation following a course of electroconvulsive therapy may prove to be a source of severe anxiety and dread."[9] As to the ultimate rationale that shock prevents suicide, one neurologist concludes that it causes at least as many suicides as it prevents.[10]

Once hospitalized, inmates certainly have to "take their medicine." In place of the ether, cyanide,[11] stupefying liquors, paraldehyde, narcotic draughts, opium, and morphine administered in lunatic asylums of the past, inmates get increasingly potent psychic energizers, tranquilizers, sedatives, and antidepressants. Hospital attendant Paul Warr's account of how a bumbling doctor comes to order varying doses of sedatives after the failure of other schemes to keep order, illustrates the potency of the restraining drugs and the capriciousness with which they are often prescribed. Warr's narrative, "Miracle Cure," is of special historical interest because it takes place around 1954, the very year in which drug companies began strong marketing of their new tranquilizing drugs. Louise Bogan's more recent account suggests that doctors are still at sea in prescribing "wonder drugs," and that the only certainty is powerful physiological action on the patient and side effects. Psychologist and drug expert Henry Lennard writes, "Basic scientists, especially pharmacologists, biochemists and physiologists, have been accumulating evidence for the view that though drugs may have specific physiological effects, their effects upon behavior and experience are largely nonspecific."[12]

In their efforts to control the inmates, attendants and nurses distribute extra and even totally unauthorized sedatives.[13] Former Boston mental hospital superintendent Walter Barton confirms that ". . . potentially dangerous drugs have been given in most public mental hospitals by persons entirely unfamiliar with the ordinary rules of drug administration.[14] Inmate civil liberties proponent David Ferleger revealed at Senate hearings on drugs in institutions that "a psychiatric attendant at Philadelphia State Hospital testified in a deposition that he forcibly injected Thorazine into my client while my client was naked, being held down in a seclusion room by two other attendants . . . upon the direction of a nurse who said that he was afraid of this particular patient."[15]

Inmates do cleverly evade swallowing medication,[16] but if they resist outright, they face more than a "bitter pill." Pseudopatient Anthony Brandt reports: "Try to refuse medicine in a state hospital today and four burly attendants will grab you, one for each limb, and spread you out on the floor while a nurse gives you a double- or triple-dose injection in your butt."[17]

Actual physical punishment is meted out covertly, so its true incidence is unknown: "On the ward attendants delivered verbal and occasionally serious physical abuse to patients in the presence of other observing patients, some of whom (the pseudopatients) were writing it all down. Abusive behavior, on the other hand, terminated quite abruptly when other staff members were known to be coming. Staff are credible witnesses. Patients are not."[18] When social worker Alma Stone stood helplessly with a group of inmates, abuse did occur, as she laments in "The Wrong Lesson." Assaults by inmates are rarely serious: "Nearly all incidents involved minor violence, e.g., pushing, scratching, and kicking."[19] Inmates assault one another more often than they assault staff.[20] If an inmate commits the cardinal sin of attacking an attendant, however, the latter will likely retaliate, even though only enough force to subdue the inmate is allowed officially.

There is a great discrepancy indeed between attendants' behavior and the impression conveyed by this "Creed for Psychiatric Aides" formulated in a training program for attendants: "I dedicate my life to the companionship of men and women of broken spirit. With humility, I accept the patient as my sacred trust. His behavior is mine to understand and to accept without personal insult or judgment. I will befriend the patient against his illness."[21] Sociologist Erving Goffman saw the real situation as a participant observer in a mental hospital: "In total institutions there is a basic split between a large managed group, conveniently called inmates, and a small supervisory staff. . . . Each grouping tends to conceive of the other in terms of narrow hostile stereotypes, staff often seeing inmates as bitter, secretive, and untrustworthy, while inmates often see staff as condescending, highhanded, and mean. Staff tends to feel superior and righteous; inmates tend, in some ways at least, to feel inferior, weak, blameworthy, and guilty."[22] Compare how the orderly in Robbie Skeist's account, "The French Kiss and the Pinch," is himself made to feel blameworthy and guilty when he allows an inmate to kiss him.

The inmate's position is exacerbated by hospital rules that are flexible enough for staff members to use them to their own advantage: "In general, punishments are not spelled out, and most rules can be stretched, negotiated, argued, ignored, or applied at convenient moments."[23] In addition, having control over everyday inmate privileges such as extra allotments of toilet paper and tobacco gives them real power over ward affairs, as doctor-inmate Marks documents in "Hosprison." An attendant may even "guest" an inmate on a worse ward during an "emergency." This informal arrangement, called back-warding, can last for most of the inmate's stay.

While attendants and nurses institute unauthorized medical procedures to suit their own convenience, they also avoid decisions by insisting that certain inmate requests are "up to the doctor," who in turn may refer requests back to the ward staff, or to his superiors. Staff members routinely pass the buck to deny their responsibility for various hospital problems, as British mental hospital superintendent David Clark shows in his account of mismanagement of ward heating, "Mutual Fury." The inherent bureaucratic inefficiency of the institutional setting, together with lack of real caring, thwart genuine attempts to make inmates comfortable.

The inmates understand that institutional regimentation serves to restrain and punish them, even if it is called treatment. Medical historian Charles Mercier states ". . . the actual word punishment is taboo, and as long as it is not used, the persons who inflict the punishments deny, in all sincerity, that punishment is inflicted."[24] The chastised inmates know that the age-old tyrannies of isolation, restraint, and punishment are being imposed "in the name of mental health" (the title of Ronald Leifer's 1969 book). Superintendent Clark writes, "In the old mental hospital wards, punishment was openly discussed. There was a range of penalties for misbehaviour starting from withdrawal of privileges and passing through seclusion, restraint, wet packs, to ECT [electroconvulsive therapy] and leucotomy [psychosurgery]. When staff became more sophisticated they became ashamed of the ward 'punishment' and would explain that the procedure was therapeutic, that it was being done for the patients' own good. Few of the patients appeared to believe this."[25]

The hospital's perennial solution to treatment problems is better and newer treatments: "Theories of human behavior which have seemed so relevant in treating neurotics, such as psychoanalysis and nondirective therapy, flounder when encountering the institutional psychotic. It seems that every type of explanation has already been proposed, applied, and found wanting in its general application, including psychotherapy, group dynamics, recreation therapy [see Carl Solomon's description of a "therapeutic" Halloween masquerade ball, "Condemned Dreams"], vocational therapy, etc. One feels compelled to do something—anything—to assist this forsaken segment of humanity."[26] The stage is set for unprincipled therapy, such as the deception Milton Rokeach and his associates practice to change the thinking of the delusive Christ ("I Don't Believe in Mental Torture"), and the "harassment therapy" that sociologist Stannard observes ("Stupid Girl. Stupid Girl. Scrub. Scrub. Scrub.") The healing fervor can escalate to justify compulsory sterilization and frightful lobotomy, the latter described by Dr. Eileen Walkenstein in "Vegetables Don't Cry." Psychiatrist Peter Breggin claims that psychosurgery has returned in a "second wave."[27]

Hospitalization itself takes away the individual's basic freedoms: "Powerlessness was visible everywhere, from the psychiatric labels to loss of freedom of movement, abuse, lack of privacy, and depersonalization to the extent that inmates are often treated as if they were invisible. Rather than being medical, then, admission and treatment are coincident with deprivation of power."[28] Confronted with sparse living quarters, dirty bathrooms, locked doors,[29] and no secure convenient place for personal possessions, the inmate feels a sense of helplessness. In the typical case at one elite hospital, "The patient's total hospital experience tended to consolidate his adverse power position (as a passive victim) in return for providing moderate indulgences in affection."[30]

Hospitalization perpetuates the inmate's passivity: "Patients continue to experience the demands of occupational roles, pseudofamilial roles, economic scarcity, political powerlessness, and interpersonal adjustments. If difficulty in facing the demands of living with limited choices and resources is part of the reason why people are in mental hospitals, they unfortunately must face the same situation when they get there," observes psychologist Robert Perrucci.[31] Even when they ostensibly have a say about hospital living conditions as part of "patient government," inmates barely influence the outcome of the minor issues they are left to debate, as in Jane Fry's account of the imbroglio over stolen cigarettes, "Patient Government." The staff view is that chronics, in particular, need to depend on hospital routine—though Dr. Marshall Edelson describes in "Back Ward" a startling experience with a group of deteriorated inmates whom he asked to help him. In "Schizophrenia Chronic Undifferentiated Type," attendant Jackie Daymoon tells of a ward in which old people are denied human contact. The late Dr. David Vail, strong advocate of deinstitutionalization, reports the pathetic case of an inmate who has been denied choice so long that she has to be taught the simplest tasks while being readied for release, in the selection titled "Vertical Extraction."

The issue is not whether treatment "works." Accounts vary. Professor Killian tells how well he responded to a short hospitalization in "Rebirth in a Therapeutic Community." Sarah Lorenz, in "Mother-Son Symbiosis" tells of being driven to despair in a "therapeutic milieu." The issue is not even whether alternatives to hospitalization are superior. The real issue is the right of non-criminals to refuse treatment or to give entirely voluntary informed consent to hospitalization, in the same way that true medical patients accept and refuse treatment.

"Anger, Loneliness, Detachment, and Boredom"

WILLIAM A. WEITZ

As part of his graduate training in psychology, Weitz entered the psychiatric ward at Walter Reed Army Hospital. He was quickly caught up in the patient role and associated little with his staff colleagues. Soon he felt bored and had a strong sense of constraint. He became angry and fearful about his sense of helplessness. The loss of a sense of personal control so affected him that he took solace in anticipating his release at the end of twenty-four hours. He learned from his experience how strongly patients' feelings and behavior are influenced by the immediate ward environment, and he implores staff to take this effect into account when evaluating patients.

A former Boston mental hospital superintendent, Walter Barton, reports that staff apathy can induce apathy in the patients, and describes how the patient culture takes over in giving support to the new admittee: "Indifference and apathy is a principal obstacle to functional efficiency. For example, at one point in the development of our hospital program, we assigned a person unknown to the ward staff to learn how the institution was seen through the patient's eyes. No one received the patient, interpreted what was expected of him, told him where he was to sleep or what his schedule would be or in any way offered him security. The patient culture 'took over' to carry out these functions because of the staff vacuum."[1]

MY INITIAL feelings of apprehension and uncertainty I believe to be natural, inasmuch as I had not spent much time with schizophrenic patients other than brief interactions on locked hospital wards. After all, this was to be a full 24 hours with these patients in a ward environment. Shortly following my entrance on the ward, I changed from my uniform into the blue convalescent pajamas required to be worn by new Ward 108 patients, and from that point on I was one of them. Gradually, I found my initial fears lessening, being replaced by a curiosity about the people with whom I was living. Interestingly enough, I did not find myself speaking to or interacting with the ward staff to the degree that I had anticipated, but rather I was more comfortable remaining alone, feeling out my role with the other patients. I had previously expected to spend most of my day talking and associating largely with staff personnel, for I would later be working with them. But, surprisingly, this was not to be the case.

Instead I spent my day in activities consistent with the status of a ward patient, only I was not "playing a patient" but was actually beginning to feel like one. I became bored and restless, and a sense of constraint became increasingly intense. Suddenly tremendous feelings of anger overwhelmed me as I sensed a loss of personal control over my life. These feelings were very genuine, despite the fact that my time on the ward was only to be for a specified 24-hour period.

I was jealous of those staff people who could come and go on the ward, those individuals with a sense of their own freedom. I resented being bound by a situation which had taken personal control away from me. Happily, these feelings of anger soon passed, and I again found myself in a solemn, quiet mood. Although interacting with the other ward patients, I felt somewhat alone. It was in this pensive mood that I started to question if my experiences were common to the other ward patients. My thoughts drifted to the next morning when I would be free to leave the ward. Feelings of comfort accompanied my thoughts of regaining a sense of independence and the ability to make my own life decisions. I found it important to maintain these thoughts, as they gave me something to grasp on to during my feelings of loss. I wondered what it must be like to be a patient on a ward without having the slightest idea about when you might be released. I questioned the kind of feelings that might be experienced by a patient in such a situation. These thoughts depressed me.

The remainder of the night passed slowly, with continual boredom accompanying my state of detachment. When the lights were finally turned out, sleep was difficult. The day had seemed so long; yet I was unable to escape into sleep. With the coming of morning I rapidly departed from the ward, for I was anxious to regain control over my behavior. I experienced a great emotional lift upon closing the ward doors behind me, and it was hard to accept that it had only been 24 short hours since I had last walked alone on the hospital grounds.

Looking back on my experience as a patient, I find that a number of significant thoughts have crystallized. My first realization was a recognition of the power of a particular role over one's behavior. It was an extraordinary feeling recognizing the extent to which being defined as a patient on the ward controlled my actions. The clothes I wore, the people with whom I was identified, the atmosphere of the ward—all these things notably influenced the way I responded in the situation. In fact, people who were not aware of my reason for being on the ward were unable to differentiate me from other ward patients. As significantly noted, I was not pretending to play the role of a patient, but found myself caught up in actually experiencing myself as one. My reactions on the ward were very much different from what I had anticipated, for I found it difficult to escape from the constraints which I felt as a patient. It became clear to me that merely defining a person as a patient on a psychiatric ward has a very powerful influence on the way he will respond, emotionally and behaviorally. Such definitions help to determine others' expectations color their perceptions. Furthermore, people's response to patients is a function of their expectations about them. It is thus significant that the patient's defined role has intrinsic effects upon the way people will respond in a psychiatric ward situation.

I also became aware of a person's need to maintain a sense of control over his own existence. I found the loss of control over my own life to be the greatest threat that I experienced as a patient, even for this briefest of time periods. While one could argue that this loss might, in itself, be very comforting to someone who is schizophrenic, I feel that the total loss of ultimate control over one's own life is a very terrifying and stress-producing experience. I found myself utilizing various means of attempting to regain some sense of freedom and personal control. I now believe that the habitual questioning of ward administrators by hospitalized psychiatric patients is not simply a sign of manipulation and excessive dependence, but rather it may be an attempt by these individuals to achieve some sense of personal involvement in their life decisions, even in the most limited ways. Such responses are generally the only means available to these patients to express appropriately their need to feel in control.

Unfortunately, in the course of spending day after day with patients, professionals often tend to lose their perspective of the validity of patients' feelings and emotions. Somehow our training influences us continually to theorize and make assumptions about patients without paying attention to their more obvious human concerns. We tend to deny their overt behavior as a function of our needs to look for deeper meaning to explain their actions. While as professionals we must be aware of this deeper level of motivation, let us not forget to consider our patients as individuals who may in fact be responding to very valid personal feelings. Such feelings have much to say regarding restrictive ward procedures, for traditional ward situations do not permit patients to have much control over their eventual fate. Rather, major decisions about the patients' lives are largely determined by the ward doctor and other ward personnel. If one can accept the validity of the patient's feelings, then an effective means of coping with this issue of control would be to allow patients greater self-determination through regular ward channels. Instituting such procedures would allow patients to become actively involved in making significant decisions about their own lives, whereby they could begin overtly to accept and regain personal responsibility and control for their thoughts and actions.

A final point needs to be made regarding the nature of the feelings which I experienced. The anger, loneliness, detachment, and boredom—all of which I felt during my stay as a patient—were experienced intensely. It was difficult not to express these feelings overtly through some form of negative behavior and surprising that the other patients did not evidence much emotion on the ward. I wondered whether other ward patients were struggling to keep similiar feelings locked within themselves. In any case, I have realized that feelings which psychiatric patients experience may have strong ties to their social reality and that we cannot simply dismiss emotional experiences of these people as inappropriate affect which is a function of their basic pathology. The feelings which patients experience often result directly from immediate influences. It thus is necessary to recognize the influence of the ward situation on patients and to consider the impact of the ward experience when an evaluation about the appropriateness of patients' emotional responses is made.

c. 1971

18

"Alleviating
Schizophrenic Thinking"

LLOYD COTTER

L argely because of a food shortage and about a 20 per cent
annual morbidity rate at their mental hospital, Cotter
and his Vietnamese colleagues offered a ward of male chronics their
freedom in return for working on the grounds for three months.
Cotter electroshocked into compliance many of the men who
declined to volunteer for the work-release program. Having less
success with shock on a female ward, Cotter starved all the remaining
recalitrants into working. He naively preens that, afterwards, "I was
not struck or threatened. Instead I was greeted with smiles . . . ." He
righteously adds that they paid the inmates one cent per day for their
labor.

As to the promise to free the inmates after three months' work,
Cotter confesses, "We were sufficiently busy that we did not have
much time to worry about the problem of how we would discharge
those patients who completed their work period and then could not
be discharged because they did not have a responsible relative to
whom they could be discharged." By "happenstance" he learns that
the United States Special Forces (Green Berets) want farm laborers
for outpost forts in Viet Cong territory in order to "cut down on the
cost of air transport and provide a better diet for the soldiers." Again
the inmates "volunteer," in order to get out. Cotter rejoices that the
inmates have now become "part of the team" as he flies back to the
safety of the United States.

I TURNED my main attention to the patients on the chronic wards of
the hospital, most of whom were schizophrenics. After a discussion

with the Vietnamese psychiatrists, we decided that a mass treatment approach, utilizing operant conditioning and instituted immediately, would save many more of these patients than a more individualized approach requiring months or years before all the patients could be examined and treated. This decision was partially based on the axiom that, in general, the longer a schizophrenic is allowed to remain regressed, the less recovery one can expect.

We started the program on a ward of 130 male patients by announcing that we were interested in discharging patients to make the hospital less crowded. Who wanted to go home? About 30 patients indicated their interest. We explained to these patients that they would have to work and support themselves if they went home— that we could not send them home to live off relatives. We wanted them to work for three months or so in the hospital to prove their capability. If they would do this, we would make every effort to have them discharged. Ten or so indicated their willingness to work. The reaction of the remainder was "Work! Do you think we're crazy?"

We sent ten off to work. To all the remaining patients we announced, "People who are too sick to work need treatment. Treatment starts tomorrow—electroconvulsive treatment. It is not painful and is nothing to be afraid of. When you are well enough to work, let us know."

The next day we gave 120 unmodified electroconvulsive treatments. Although modified ECT was used on some of the patients on the admitting ward, time and drug limitations precluded its use on the chronic wards. Perhaps because of the smaller size and musculature of the Vietnamese people, no symptoms of compression fractures were reported at any time.

The treatments were continued on a three-times-a-week schedule. Gradually there began to be evident improvement in the behavior of the patients, the appearance of the ward, and the number of patients volunteering for work. This latter was a result of the ECT's alleviating schizophrenic or depressive thinking and affect with some. With others it was simply a result of their dislike or fear of ECT. In either case our objective of motivating them to work was achieved.

Reinforcement of selected behavior is the major concept of operant conditioning. Reinforcement which consists of presenting stimuli is called positive reinforcement, whereas reinforcement which consists of terminating stimuli is called negative reinforcement. It can be seen that the ECT served as a negative reinforcement for the response of work for those patients who chose to work rather than to continue receiving ECT.

The second ward where we started this procedure was a women's ward of 130 patients. Expecting the women to be more pliable, I hoped for quicker and better results. Instead, due perhaps to their greater passivity or the attitude that success in life is achieved when they can be idle, at the end of 20 treatments there were only 15 women working. We stopped the ECT then, and to the men and women still not working said, "Look. We doctors, nurses, and technicians have to work for our food, clothes, rent money, etc. Why should you have it better? Your muscles are just as good as ours. After this, if you don't work, you don't eat. Who is ready to start work immediately rather than miss any meals?"

About 12 patients made this choice. After one day without food, ten more patients volunteered for work and after two days without food, ten more. After three days without food, all the remaining patients volunteered for work. As has been repeatedly demonstrated, when the subject is hungry food is one of the strongest and most useful of positive reinforcements. This may be particularly true of schizophrenics who, as a group, tend to show enhanced interest in food.

1966

19

"Ideological Treatment"

LEONID PLYUSHCH

When arrested in 1972 for writing for clandestine Soviet publications, Leonid Plyushch had already lost his job as a mathematician for writing an "anti-Soviet" letter to a Soviet newspaper. After a year of prison interrogation and investigation, a judge convicted him of anti-Soviet activity and sentenced him to compulsory treatment at a special psychiatric prison hospital. The Serbsky Institue diagnosed "sluggish schizophrenia characterized by reformist ideas." Plyushch was then sent on to the Dnepropestrovsk "special mental hospital" as one of a number of political prisoners. Here he tells how the doctors and wardens tried to end his political dissent by harassing and drugging him into submission.

There was a great international clamor for his release, culminating in an appeal by the French Communist Party late in 1975. Early in 1976 the Soviet authorities released Plyushch at the Hungarian-Soviet border and sent him and his family to Vienna by train. He went on to Paris, where he began work on behalf of Soviet dissenters. Soviet activists Zhores Medvedev, General Petr Grigorenki, and Valery Tarsis (see the Admission section) have also suffered psychiatric oppression. For other examples, see Vladimir Petrov's "Experimenting for the NKVD: A Prison-Camp Brigadier Learns How Soviet Psychiatrists Turn Sane Men into Gibbering Idiots;" Cornelia Mee's *The Internment of Soviet Dissenters in Mental Hospitals;* Subcommittee to Investigate the Administration of the Internal Security Act's report; *Abuse of Psychiatry for Political Repression in the Soviet Union;* and Peter Reddaway's *Uncensored Russia: Protest and Dissent in the Soviet Union* and *Victims of Soviet Psychiatric Abuse Since Late 1972: A Preliminary Dossier.*

THE HORROR of a *psikhushka* (mad house) gripped me from the start. In the ward there were more patients than beds. I was put as the third person on two bunks that had been pushed together. On the beds patients were writhing from haloperidol. One man's tongue was lolling out, another man was rolling his eyes, a third walked around unnaturally bent over. Some lay and groaned with the pain—they had been given injections of sulphur. As they explained to me, they were being punished for bad behaviour.

All the patients walked around in their underclothes, which were without buttons. I felt embarrassed in front of the nurses, as one's genitals were visible in these 'clothes'. Patients stood around the door and begged the orderlies to let them go to the lavatory.

When I woke up next morning, I saw two orderlies beating up a patient. In the afternoon I was summoned for interrogation by Dr. Kamenetskaya. An orderly came in and said that a patient had attacked some orderlies and had then tried to hang himself in the lavatory. The doctor ordered him to be tied up, and burst into the ward and started shouting at him.

The patients told me that he hadn't attacked anyone, but he had been beaten up because he had asked to go to the lavatory. But no one could make up his mind to tell the doctor about this because they were afraid of being punished with sulphur. The patients began to make fun of the victim, but he told them: 'They'll beat you up too, you know.'

I had arrived at the prison with a group of thieves, who were feigning illness in order to 'have a rest' and a good feed. On the second day they all admitted that they were quite healthy—they were horrified by what they had seen.

A week later I was taken to another floor. Here the regulations were not so strict—hardly anyone was writhing in pain from haloperidol; it was easy to get to the lavatory, the patients wore dirty, ragged clothes; but they were pyjamas . . . .

They put me on a plank bunk between two patients—one man was seriously ill and had completely lost any resemblance to a human being (he was swollen, defecated where he lay and spent his time masturbating). As he was dying he was soon transferred to an ordinary hospital. This is a common practice designed to bring down the death statistics.

The political prisoners immediately explained to me that you shouldn't complain here. If you did you were given intensified treatment with neuroleptics and injections of sulphur, and they prevented you from going to the lavatory.

You had to admit to the doctors that you were ill and renounce your views. At the beginning I argued with them, but then I came to the conclusion that they were right.

I met a journalist from Leningrad called Evdokimov, a member of the NTS.* We began to have ideological arguments. They broke us up, saying we were *antisovietchiki*. One of the orderlies told the patients we were 'yids'. Several patients began to complain that we prevented them from sleeping during the day. I was put in another ward. There was a political prisoner there as well. But the doctors warned him not to speak to me. He didn't.

One very sick patient who was known as 'Mister' used to yell out anti-Soviet slogans and asked me to correct his delirious letters to the Soviet authorities. The orderlies promised to 'smuggle them out' secretly and in return took all his food parcels from outside. He died after two months.

The orderlies in the hospital were criminals serving out their sentences. They demand groceries, socks, etc., from the patients, in return for which they allow you an extra visit to the lavatory or increase your ration of tobacco. If you refused to give them the bribe they might beat you up. They beat Evdokimov up for this. I complained to the doctor and things got worse. They searched me several times a day and took away my tobacco. I had to give them bribes.

According to the rules they take you to the lavatories in groups six times a day and during three of the visits you are allowed to smoke. The patients try to smoke as much as they possibly can, and as a result often vomit.

I was prescribed haloperidol in small doses. I became drowsy and apathetic. It became difficult to read books. I started to secretly spit out tablets.

After three months they put me in the worst department—No. 9. Here the arbitrary rule of the orderlies is less evident, but to make up for it the 'treatment' is much more intense. You are under more strict supervision and the doctor's interrogation becomes more humiliating.

*Usual translation is 'Popular Labour Alliance', a Russian anti-Soviet emigre organisation based in Frankfurt and Paris.

I was put in a so-called 'supervised ward' where they put the serious violent cases—some fight, others writhe in epileptic fits, one cries, another roars with laughter, another sings thieves' songs, another describes his case and his sexual adventures in a loud voice, another asks to go to the lavatory—in short, bedlam.

Then one of the 'border-crossers' asks to go to the lavatory. He is incontinent and has the doctor's permission to go at any time. But the orderlies do not take this into account, so he urinates on the floor in the ward. He is not the only one who uses this form of protest . . . .

In the lavatories the picture is even more depressing—it is full of people, there's a fight for a place at the 'peep-hole', people search for cigarette stubs among the used lavatory paper. Some of the patients also eat their excrement or masturbate. I don't want to blacken the picture—this last did not happen every day.

I was considered the most dangerous patient in the hospital. The orderlies and nurses were forbidden to talk to me. The other political prisoners were warned that if they talked to me it would be the worse for them. When one orderly started to take science fiction books from me he was told that he was associating with an *antisovietchik*. For two days I sat next to a political prisoner in the dining-room, but they moved us to different tables.

Once I talked to a young murderer for a whole evening—about science fiction. The next day he was put in another ward. What is more, the doctors reproached me for making friends with another murderer, which was completely untrue. At the same time they reproached me for not talking to any of the patients. To keep me in complete isolation I was forbidden to go to the kitchen or into the yard in case I might accidentally meet other politicals.

Even eight months before my trial, instructions were given to the Dnepropetrovsk prison that I was not to have any contact whatsoever with the doctor from Kiev, Plakhotnyuk.

At the interviews, the doctors asked me about my contacts outside. I told them that these questions were interrogator's questions and refused to answer them. The interviews themselves were very painful for me as they discussed my beliefs and made humiliating comments about them. They commented on my letters and the letters to my relatives. When my wife complained about something in the behaviour of my elder son and praised the younger son, they told me that the elder was on the right track whereas the younger was schizophrenic. They hinted that my wife wasn't normal either. And as for a close woman friend who wrote me affectionate letters, she was supposed to be my mistress and so they would not give me her letters.

In general the doctors suggested I cease writing to all my friends as they were all *antisovietchiki* and my correspondence with them proved that on leaving the hospital I would continue my 'anti-Soviet activities'.

After the Yakir-Krasin trial they suggested I write a confession. I asked them, 'Do you really think that an adult can change his views so quickly? They must be lying.'* The doctor agreed that they lied but continued to put pressure on me to recant.

But a confession was not enough; there had to be proof that it was genuine, and there had to be proof why I considered I was mentally ill. I answered the last question carefully, saying that I was not a specialist and that I could not express an opinion about my own illness. Here it must be taken into account that I did not know their diagnosis and did not know what I should be disputing.

A few words about doctors—their moral and intellectual level.
A patient: When will I be let out?
Doctor: Not until I'm on a pension.

One of the patients called the doctors Gestapo-ists. They prescribed injections of sulphur. (After an injection of sulphur your temperature goes up to 40°C, the place where you had the injection is very painful, you cannot get away from the pain. Many people get haemorrhoids as a result of sulphur injections.) This patient groaned loudly for twenty-four hours. Mad with pain, he tried to hide himself under the bed; in despair he broke the window and tried to cut his throat with the glass. Then he was punished again and beaten up. He kept asking everyone: 'Am I going to die?' and only when he really did begin to die, and another patient noticed it, did they stop the sulphur. And for two days they gave him oxygen and brought him various medicines. They saved him. As I understood, the use of sulphur was counter-indicated for him.

In a nearby section a patient, a common-law criminal, told the doctors that three political prisoners (one of whom was dumb) 'are having anti-Soviet conversations'. These patients were suspected of

---

*Yakir and Krasin were two Soviet dissenters arrested in 1972. After some months in prison they were induced to recant and to give the KGB extensive information about their fellow-dissenters.

plotting. When they searched the dumb one they found a note: 'And how much do oranges cost?' This was regarded as a coded message. They began to inject into the veins of the 'conspirators' doses of barbamyl, hitherto unheard-of in the hospital. They were brought into the ward completely unconscious. At the same time they began to give them sulphur, without any explanation. And then we heard about the 'conspiracy' in a roundabout way.

Dr. E. N. Kamenetskaya, whom the patients called Ilse Koch,* boasted in front of Evdokimov that she had bought Remarque. He gave her the nickname 'Remarque'. Someone reported the nickname, and Evdokimov was then put on haloperidol.

Doctor Lyubarskaya† said to me: 'You are just an ordinary person—why did you go in for politics?' I explain that one of the ideas of the communists was the involvement of all working people in political activity. The Bolsheviks were ordinary people too. Answer: 'But you're not a Bolshevik', and she goes on to explain: 'Your abnormality is shown by the way you have always from an early age been concerned with things that were none of your business' (she was thinking of my activities at school when I took part in the Brigade which helped the border guards; then I was in the vigilantes who went after thieves, speculators and prostitutes—that is, I was an active Komsomol member).

The following episode says a great deal about the professional standards of the doctors. I asked the same doctor: 'Why is psychotherapy not used in this hospital?' Answer: 'There is no use for psychotherapy in psychiatry.'

I have described what I heard and saw. But I was asked to describe what it was like before I was there.

The conditions for both the sick patients and the sane ones were much worse. The orderlies used to beat them up for the slightest thing, and they nearly beat them to death.

The doctor in charge of my case, Dr. Lyubarskaya, was the head of a department. In her department the orderlies killed a patient. The incident was hushed up and the orderlies were sent off to a camp. Lyubarskaya was transferred to our department as a simple doctor.

At the beginning of the 1970s the male nurses destroyed the liver of a political prisoner called Grigoriev by beating, and he died.

---

*Name of a notorious Nazi extermination-camp doctor.
†Dr. L.A. Lyubarskaya is mistakenly called L.A. Chasovskikh in the *Chronicle* and some other sources.

Obviously such incidents led to 'a relaxation in the regulations'. I cannot check these stories, but I heard about this from political prisoners whose sanity I do not doubt and from ordinary criminals.

To sum up—what is the aim of such 'treatment' and regulations? I saw in my own case that the first days are meant to break a person morally straight away, break down his will to fight. Then begins the 'treatment' with neuroleptics. I was horrified to see how I deteriorated intellectually, morally and emotionally from day to day. My interest in political problems quickly disappeared, then my interest in scientific problems, and then my interest in my wife and children. This was replaced by fear for my wife and children. My speech became jerky and abrupt. My memory also deteriorated.

At first I felt it keenly when I saw the patients' suffering or learned that some friends had turned traitor. Then I became indifferent to it. The effect of the neuroleptics increased my isolation from the healthy politicals. I did not want to hear the cries, the fights, the laughter, the crying, the delirium. For whole days on end I lay and tried to sleep. The neuroleptics helped me.

I did not have a thought in my head. The only thoughts that remained were—the lavatory, smoking, and the 'bribes' you had to give the orderlies to get an extra visit to the lavatory. And one other thought—that I must remember everything I saw there, so I could describe it later. Alas, I didn't remember a hundredth part of what I saw.

1973-1976

20

"Worry Warts"

IVAN BELKNAP

Sociologist Belknap observed how attendants decided which inmates would get shock treatments in a large state mental hospital in Texas. This treatment is not so dramatic nowadays, since the subjects generally get muscle relaxants—which sometimes paralyze their breathing.

ANOTHER STRONG disciplinary device used on Ward 30, and one of much wider significance in the maintenance of order, makes use of the hospital's electroshock therapy (EST). This therapy is under strict medical administration by the professional team of ward physician and nurse, who come on the ward twice each week with the attendant supervisor to give the treatment.

Patients who are to receive this treatment are selected by the physician and by the first charge attendant. On the day before the shock team is scheduled, the charge attendant makes out the EST List, as it is called. He lists for treatment those patients he feels need the treatment because they are "acting up," are causing trouble, have become disturbed, or show strong evidence of becoming disturbed or violent. In addition to these patients, there are three or four patients who are on the list more or less routinely for what is called in the ward "maintenance therapy." These are patients who have had a continuous history of violence or disturbance on the ward since admission until they are put on a shock series which may last for as long as 3 months. The amnesia and disorientation produced in these patients by the shock treatment keeps them quiet and prevents their disturbing or hurting the other patients and upsetting the ward routine.

On all the lists for shock made up by Mr. Albright or Mr. Knight [charge attendants], there were always several patients who were on the list for insubordination to the attendants or to a ward helper or for having fought each other. If both the patients in the fight were in the fifth or sixth levels, both were shocked. If one of the patients was in the fourth level and the other from the lower levels, both were held responsible, but the fourth-level [most privileged], patient was usually given admonition and temporary loss of some privilege, while the lower-level patient was put on the shock list. The probability of the punitive use of shock treatment varies inversely with status in Ward 30, except for a few patients selected by Dr. Baker for individual attention.

On Ward 30 it was evident that two concepts of the use of shock therapy were both being used. The formal purpose of the treatments was medical and therapeutic, but they depended for their execution on the cooperation of the attendants. They were thus open to uses which were disciplinary rather than therapeutic. In the last analysis, the physician had to take the attendant's word for it that the patient had been acting up, since the physician spent little time on the ward. To an observer who had been on the ward during the week it would be clear that two or three patients were on the list because they had responded with normal resentment to actual ill treatment by an attendant or another patient, or because they objected to the hospital food by refusing to eat it. The sixth-level hallucinatory and delusional "worry warts" were particularly likely to be put on the shock lists. One senior attendant said frankly that he put one of these patients on the list to give himself and the ward a rest from a particularly boring story.

The rule on Mr. Albright's list was, however, generally that any patient who deviated too far from his position in the status system was put on the shock list and told why. This was not done in a spirit of deception. Mr. Albright considered sincerely that any patient who did deviate from ward routine was thereby showing signs of mental disturbance. The maintenance of the system of ward statuses required the elimination of such deviation. Furthermore, as Mr. Albright said, the shock treatment was good for nearly all mental patients because it kept them from worrying so much about themselves and actually improved their physical health.

The new attendant who kept his eyes on the effects of shock therapy in Ward 30 could see for himself its effectiveness as a threat in maintaining order. Most of the patients who had been on the ward more than a few weeks were afraid of the treatment; those who had not experienced it were if anything more afraid of it than those who had. For most patients the threat of being put on the shock list had an instant effect in bringing their conduct into line with the requirements of their position in the ward.

The source of the patients' fear of shock therapy could not in fact have come with their personal experience of the therapy, since amnesia for this experience is almost complete. But among both patients and attendants there is widely circulated knowledge of the administration of the treatment and its effect on the patient. This knowledge is based on the fact that some of the patients in Ward 30 have assisted the shock team in the administration of therapy to patients, holding them down, and helping to strap them in bed, or watching them after they have quieted. The administration of shock on the ward is often carried out in full sight of a group of interested onlookers. The patient's convulsions often resemble those of an accident victim in death agony and are accompanied by choking gasps and at times a foaming overflow of saliva from the mouth. The patient slowly recovers without memory of the occurrence, but he has served the others as a frightful spectacle of what may be done to them. Moreover, in the early disorientation and vacuity of his state of recovery he is obviously upsetting to the other patients. Patients who have not seen shock treatment are provided with detailed descriptions by those who have.

In addition to the specific knowledge about shock therapy in Ward 30, there is a fearsome mythology that also circulates among some of the patients and attendants. Most patients and attendants are persuaded that the treatment is probably beneficial, but there are said to be risks of broken backs, mortal heart attacks, and brain injury from the convulsions. Tales are told of old men who were killed by the strain of the treatment and of patients who could not get well under the treatment and who had to be shocked so many times that both mind and body disintegrated completely. Since no explanation of shock therapy is attempted by the professionals or the attendants, while the treatment itself is not concealed, some such mythology is to be expected. The mythology of Ward 30 has grown through the years and plays a strong part in the disciplinary effectiveness of shock therapy in the ward social system.

c. 1954

21

"Sixty Comas"

R. FREDERICK WEST

After Reverend Frederick West came to believe that hostile congregants at his Raleigh, North Carolina, Disciples of Christ Church were trying to destroy him with radio waves, he "went to pieces" while delivering a sermon. His wife witnessed the debacle: "As he stood in the pulpit, at times preaching eloquently, and at other times lapsing into personal narrative which had little meaning to the majority, I felt as though my body were being lashed with a whip."

Logan Pearsall Smith tells of an old vicar whose flock was scandalized when the cleric "gradually introduced certain alterations into the Church services. These had been vaguely supposed at the time to be of a High Church character, but afterward they were put down to a growing mental derangement, which had finally culminated at the infamous Harvest Festival, when his career as a clergyman of the Church of England had ended. On this painful occasion the old man had come into church outlandishly dressed and had gone through a service with chanted gibberish and unaccustomed gestures, and prayers which were unfamiliar to the congregation."[1] Because the former don had lapsed into his scholarly specialty of primitive Greek religious rites, he disappeared a few days later, and some thought he was "shut up in an asylum for the insane."

Reverend West also disappeared a few days after his unfamiliar sermon, first to Graylyn, a private mental hospital at Winston-Salem, North Carolina, for a few weeks, and then to Dix Hill State Hospital at Raleigh early in 1954.

In the selection, he deplores the arbitrariness and dangerousness of the "optimum" sixty deep insulin comas that his doctor insisted he undergo, after pronouncing the reverend "schizophrenic with paranoid tendencies." He damns the deceit and hypocrisy of the doctors who say that shock treatments are "nothing more than going to sleep." Having experienced the confusion and discomfort following shock that he describes here so well, Reverend West ". . . often wished that the doctors had a few comas themselves before describing them so glibly to others."

THE PART of the treatments which I loathed the most was when I was revived to consciousness. Seldom could I identify my own hands and feet as belonging to my body. I felt completely disintegrated, literally all to pieces. Seconds and minutes seemed like centuries while I desperately struggled to restore my identity. Being strapped to the bed when I craved to get up was equally frustrating. Most of the times my memory was erased, and my mind blurred as far as rational thought was involved. When this happened, I was frightened and helpless beyond description. In addition my thirst was insatiable even after drinking the usual three glasses of sugary, canned orange juice. The experiences were more trying than my former nightmares.

Eventually, I became obsessed with the fear that I might not recover from one of the treatments. I did not fear death; I had accepted the Lord as my Shepherd. But I was afraid that after some treatment I might only "come to" just enough for my mind to remain permanently confused, fragmented, or irrational. I was anxious to retain what "clearing up" and some degree of recovery had already been achieved. Also, I was puzzled as to why the staff had not voluntarily told me what diagnosis had been made by the staff meeting for that purpose. And it did not make sense to me that the staff would not allow us patients to lie down in bed and rest or sleep after exhausting treatments. I could hardly keep my eyes open when I fought tiredness and drowsiness for hours every afternoon. (This policy was out of line with rest recommended for insulin shock patients, just as for T.B. patients, by experts.)

I had gathered all the information I could about the various schools of insulin theory and treatments. As I considered the varieties of approach, I debated with myself: "Why are sixty comas necessary at State Hospital for insulin shock patients? Why not thirty or one hundred? At one hospital they administer light shocks, not giving sufficient insulin to burn up enough of the body's sugar content to allow a patient to reach the coma level. At another hospital, they do give deep insulin shock treatments, but they vary the number required for individual patients according to the needs and responses of the persons involved. I favor the latter practice myself, for they combine personal work by psychiatrists with shock treatments to determine the patient's possible needs for further insulin therapy. I question State Hospital's extreme theory and practice of requiring sixty comas for every insulin ward patient, regardless of the progress or condition of any individual. This may be all right for hogs on a mass basis, but why for *people?* Why this impersonal nonhuman approach without any use of psychiatry directly with the human patient?"

1954

22

"Miracle Cure"

PAUL WARR

Journalist Warr took a job as an attendant in a large British mental hospital. In a refractory ward called the "Block," he saw a psychiatrist have the padded rooms dismantled and then initiate a hydrotherapy fiasco and a sedation program that backfired. The shuffling somnolence caused by the sedatives prevails in present-day mental hospitals.

PADDED ROOMS were a firm favourite with nurses who lacked any understanding of patients. A patient who shouted, fussed and fought was the object of close attention and observation. It was a rule that the doctor should be consulted before the padded room was brought into use. This, like other rules, was open to abuse, and it was a commonplace for a student nurse to manhandle a patient into the pad merely because the man had stuck out his tongue or refused to clean a bed space. Another regulation decreed that patients should be kept in these stuffy, airless rooms only from 7 p.m. to 7 a.m.—throughout the night, in other words. This was frequently disobeyed, and I have known patients spend as long as two or even three days in the pad with only brief, well-guarded visits to the toilet. Worse, I saw three or four patients put together in one pad and left for a whole day. Nurses were careless of patients left in the padded rooms and meals for them were a hit or miss affair. One man was without food and drink for a whole day before the charge nurse suddenly remembered his responsibilities. His remark, 'Well it'll weaken the bastard, and we might get some peace at last,' summed up the current attitude. The fact that the patient was a diabetic did not seem to worry him.

"MIRACLE CURE"

Towards the end of my tour of duty in the Block one of the senior psychiatrists came to the conclusion that padded rooms were all very well in their place, but our hospital was not the place for them. He lost no time in approaching the medical superintendent with ideas culled directly from American mental health journals in which it was said that all forms of restraint could be successfully abolished. The superintendent was in full agreement that they were archaic in conception and practically useless in practice, the only service being that they helped nurses in the execution of ward discipline and control. The senior psychiatrist was overjoyed to realise that he had made a convert to the progressive school of thought. A week later, while removal of the padded rooms was under active consideration, he suggested that we bring into use an elaborate bath with sprays at the sides and an ingenious contrivance for saturating patients first with hot then with cold water. This had been installed along with the rest of the standard fitments when the hospital was built. Hydrotherapy is now largely discredited. It was once believed that total immersion in water of different temperatures could have an invigorating or pacifying effect on certain types of insanity. It would be pointless to labour the analogy to sixteenth-century witch-ducking in village ponds. Schools of psychiatric thought advance slowly and precariously on slender assumptions.

While we were busy implementing his suggestion and getting ourselves thoroughly soaked while wrestling with protesting patients in the newly dubbed Hydrotherapy Room, workmen arrived to remove the padded rooms. This was a major operation involving structural alterations to part of the building. Great wads of rubber and horsehair padding lay strewn about in one corridor. At least one patient helped himself to handfuls to experimentally chew. The workmen watched the 'loonies' with an air of amusement while we tried to run the ward as the senior psychiatrist evidently wanted it run.

Presently, when all the padded rooms had been removed and the resultant areas furnished as ordinary side rooms with beds, tables and chairs for the well-behaved patients, one charge nurse approached the instigator of these changes to point out that hydrotherapy did not seem to be having much effect except that we were all going home with wet trousers and saturated shoes. Next day the psychiatrist sent down three pairs of swimming trunks and a note to the effect that we should be properly garbed when administering the treatment. Later he drew up a number of complex forms, one for each patient having water treatment. The charge nurse on duty was required to complete these and submit them for scrutiny. Things were getting quite desperate when something went wrong with the water supply and hydrotherapy came to an end, never to return. We were most thankful, because it had taken up several days to find the water main and effectively sabotage it.

If one problem was solved, another quickly sprang into being. With the absence of padded rooms our work increased. Refractory patients had to be watched continuously lest they should suddenly abuse their new-found freedom. They, at least, sensed that we were very worried about the consequences of progress. It did not take them long to start playing up. Windows were broken daily, sheets and blankets ripped to shreds while our backs were turned. The day room was in a constant tumult. I began to dread going on duty in the ward, not so much because I might become involved in a brawl as because the round-the-clock row deafened me. Every day room had its own loudspeaker extension from a central radio located somewhere in the administration building. It was one of the first sounds to be heard in the morning. Once, when an announcer said that morning prayers would be heard in a few seconds, a patient picked up a plate of fried bread and sausages and hurled it at the speaker. There was a tremendous crash and the announcer's voice stopped as though snipped off with sharp scissors. The patient bawled: 'What we want that for? God's not here! They won't let Him in here because He's not as mad as the rest of us. He's doing His job, forgiving sins!' The loud-speaker was later restored, but not in its original condition. By the time it had been repaired it was impossible to distinguish the human voice from the B.B.C. Symphony Orchestra. The hodgepodge of noise now merged with those patients who once brooded out their angry hours in padded rooms, the crash of breaking windows and the moans and groans of those in mental anguish. A spell of duty in such an atmosphere made one glad to flee into the surrounding countryside, where the only sound was the cry of the curlew over the ploughed fields. There was little one could do about it. In exasperation I once bawled: 'For God's sake, shut up, all of you!' A little old fellow sitting near looked up in amazement and protested: 'I wasn't saying anything, nurse.' He gave me such a reproachful look that I walked out in despair, leaving them to get on with their noise-making.

"MIRACLE CURE"

The eventual solution came not because we complained to the psychiatrist that his progressive methods were driving *us* crazy but because he happened to be passing through the day room and was attacked by two vehement gentlemen whose proper place was on a political platform at a public meeting. They agreed that he was a reincarnation of Lenin and determined to do away with him at the first opportunity. When he escaped he rushed up to me and demanded: 'Is it always like this?'

'Always the same, sir,' I said. 'You soon get used to it.' As I finished shouting at him above the noise, two windows on the other side of the room went west under the impact of a patient's fist. That settled it. The psychiatrist dashed away, vowing that he would 'do something about this shambles.' The next day he was back with the solution to our troubles: instead of restraining patients, we would sedate them! The charge nurse pointed out that this would mean about ninety per cent of the patients being in bed all day, but the psychiatrist dismissed the opinion. 'You can sedate a patient to a point where he is still capable of walking about,' he said placidly. The next thing was the arrival of the dispensary van with two large baskets containing bottles of paraldehyde for the mild cases and capsules of sodium amytl for the awkward boys. We lined this array up in the drug cupboard and got to work as soon as possible. One by one the selected patients were brought into the clinic and offered the choice of drinking an ounce of paraldehyde of their own free will or having it forced down their throats. The majority of them were already averse to the stuff; I did not blame them. It was foul-smelling and lingered on the breath for several hours after drinking. To have a patient breathing in your face after he has had paraldehyde is almost as bad as taking a dose yourself. Those who refused to drink it were forced over the wooden table, their noses gripped by one nurse while the other poured it down the gaping open gullet. In the tussle we spilled large quantities all over the floor until the surface resembled a skating rink. Several patients were punched in the stomach when they cleverly eluded the table treatment. After we finished with about a dozen of them, we opened the door to admit some fresh air. As it swung back we were greeted by solemn faces of those who had already received their doses. They stood there like puppies, wanting to know what to do next. I shepherded them into the day room and sat them all down on chairs round the walls while I stood near the fire to watch them. This, I thought, is the end to the noise. They will be all

107

right now. Then the rowdy clamour started up all over again, louder than ever. It lasted until lunch-time, when most of them had become heavy-eyed and reduced to mumbling. With difficulty they were placed at their respective tables, but most of them only toyed with their food, while some fell asleep before they could reach the pudding stage. We had to haul them into the dormitory and put them all to bed. We then spent an enjoyable afternoon, playing cards and casting appreciative glances at our tribe of snoring infants.

The aftermath—it was inevitable that there should be one—came the same evening. I was working what was called a 'long day' and did not finish until nine o'clock, when the night nurse came on duty. He took one look at the recumbent patients and exclaimed: 'Christ, you poisoned them or something? They're not usually like this.'

His troubles started about two o'clock in the morning when the effect of the sedative began to wear off. One by one the patients got out of bed, most of them believing that it was time to rise, and started wandering around the dormitory in the nude. The solitary night nurse was at his wit's end and had to phone for the night superintendent, who managed to call in more than half an hour later. He hunted about in the melee of the patients for the night nurse before hearing a shout from the clinic. The man had locked himself in there for safety after being pawed by the yawning figures who totally disregarded his orders and forgot all about discipline.

This marked the beginning of a long series of experiments on the patients by the senior psychiatrist. He varied the daily doses of sedative until most of the patients were spending their time in an unhealthy ambulatory dream. The noise died down to a depressed silence, broken only by the slithering of carpet slippers on bare linoleum. It turned out to be more nerve-racking than the former hullabaloo, but there was nothing we could do about it. The psychiatrist still insisted that sedation had a marked curative effect and produced a clipping from a medical journal which reported success in hospitals on the Continent. When it was pointed out that the experiments elsewhere had been conducted on patients of a markedly different calibre, he dismissed the observation as 'silly.'

c. 1954

23

"Wonder Drugs"

LOUISE BOGAN

Unhappy about criticism of her poetry., Louise Bogan entered The Neurological Institute in New York for a short stay early in 1931. Her friend Ruth Limmer writes, "She was recuperating in a sanitarium in Connecticut, where the therapeutic regime included weaving, needlespray showers, sunbaths, and 'most simple-minded tasks'" when she appended this poem in a letter to Edmund Wilson:

> My God, what was the crime. Did I deserve
> Therapy, out of possible punishments?
> What the betrayal, that the faded nerve
> Must bloom again by means not making sense?
> O, I shall mend! Even now I grow quite well.
> Knitting round wash-cloths on the paths of hell.

Late in 1935 Bogan wrote to Theodore Roethke, who was then in a mental hospital:

> At the Neurological Center, here in town, at one time I went through three weeks of high-class neurology myself. I had a room all done up in noncorrosive greens, and a day and a night nurse, and a private bath, and such food as you never ate, and hydrotherapy, including steam-cabinets, and a beautiful big blond doctor by the name of McKinney. I had a great triumph with McKinney; I made him shed a single tear and when you can make a neurologist shed a tear, you're doing well, as you probably know by now. . . . Well, there I was, and I got worse and worse, rather than better and better, because I hadn't come into myself as a person, and was still a puling child, hanging on to people, and trying to make them tell me the truth.

109

BLUE JOLTS

Bogan moved to Washington Heights in 1937, to an apartment overlooking The Psychiatric Institute, sister institution to The Neurological Institute. She entered The Neurological Institute again in 1965, and from there wrote Ruth Limmer the following letters, in which she wryly describes the effects of drug treatment.

> The Neurological Institute
> 710 W. 168th Street
> N.Y.C.
> June 12, 1965

DEAR RUTH:

Yes! I have moved over to this far-from-forbidding spot, after a severe seizure of pure depression, early in the week.— Dr. Wall put me in touch with a Dr. H. (who is the big anti-depressant-drug man) who is attached to the Psychiatric *and* the Neurological. And as it happened (and fortunately, I think, on the whole) a room was vacant on this, the 12th floor—the "emotionally disturbed" sector.—There is no doubt that my *depression* has become the main problem. Dr. H's pills are called "psychic renovators"—or some such term. Dr. Tyson called yesterday, and explained that these drugs went straight to the hidden sources in a most extraordinary way; they are by no means *tranquilizers.*—Yesterday, after my first doses, I became exceedingly dopey. This first effect wears off, I am told.—In any case, I have *taken action!*—And am being taken care of, down to the last detail. And am *eating!* and sleeping (fairly well). And with doctors on every side. . . .

This depressed state began last fall, I think—with the return to the scenes of my childhood—or adolescence. Boston is really filled with sorrowful memories of my family, and my early self.—I thought, because I had "insight" into it all, that I could rise above it. But H. has told me that a depression can *seep through,* as it were, in any case.

This is a most attractive set-up, with lovely *views* on all sides, and no grisly, sloppy hospital atmosphere. The patients are, of course, pretty mixed—with some exceedingly vocal ones. And the "treatments" include electric shock (which has been much "improved," I hear—but Lord preserve us).—Some young people receive these, as well as older types.—I feel that they are not for me—since my mental *confusion* is nil. (An exceedingly pretty little Italian

110

woman doctor puts one through a short stretch of baby-psychoanalysis, right away; and I was surprised to find myself subtracting *sevens,* counting backward, etc.)

   * * *

Just let us hope that the "drugs" connect with the *psyche.*

Love,
Louise

Neurological Institute
710 West 168th Street
New York, New York
June 26, 1965

Dear Ruth:

Well, I guess I'm over the worst of the fringe effects of the strange "medication" ("wonder drug") treatment. Believe me, it was rough, for about five nights: heart palpitation—the feeling of the center of the citadel being invaded. And blood pressure taken in all positions: sitting, standing, etc. And the semi-knowledge that the doctor was just as much at sea as you were. (This was nonsense, of course, as H. is tops in his field.) THEN—finally, the pill is changed, and the heart quiets down, and you say, "I'll never worry about *anything* again." One evening, with a gibbous moon hanging over the city (such *visions* we have!) like a piece of red cantaloupe, and automobiles showing red danger signals, as they receded down Ft. Wash. Ave.—I thought I had reached the edge of eternity, and *wept* and *wept.*—I'm now on a little white pill which makes me rather woozy, but is mild otherwise. . . . (I'm writing *through* it, at the moment.)

1965

24

"The Wrong Lesson"

ALMA STONE

Psychiatric social worker Stone stood immobilized when she saw an attendant pound an inmate and faded into the ring of inmates who were watching the beating. In explanation Stone recalls an earlier episode in which an inmate resisted a nurse. The nurse reported her for insubordination for not helping her drag one inmate, and Stone's supervisor told her she had a lot to learn. Stone frets whether she, like so many hospital workers, has learned indifference.

I HEARD a crash in the dining room—broken dishes. A kitchen employee came for an attendant with some urgency. I offered to help, she shook her head, said he seemed more confused than angry. No further noise. Then he came down the hall, supported on each side by an attendant. The task is by no means easy, but he was more frightened and passive than fighting. I unlocked the door of the seclusion ward for them. The ward attendants who ordinarily would have unlocked the hall door to the single rooms were not in the room. As the man on one side of the patient used one hand to get his keys and open the door, the patient struggled to the floor, pulling the other man down with him. By then a ward attendant arrived, quietly, quickly, his stance and body a message of assurance. The three of them were with him on the floor, trying to collect his flailing limbs for everyone's protection. A fourth attendant ran through the room knelt beside the patient, and with his fist pounded on his ribs.

Patients streamed to a respectful distance, perhaps fifteen to twenty men watching in a rough semicircle. All of this happened inside of two or three minutes from the moment the ward door was unlocked. I was standing by the door, moving to leave, when the struggle began. As events unfolded, I stood immobilized; I did not know what to do. I did not dare go to the group on the floor; who would agree that the authority was mine? Only humanity, but that was a voice unheard under the hospital gestures of silence and control. I could not stand there as an employee; I put my keys in my pocket and moved into the ring of patients. I wanted to cry. Patients and I looked mutely and tensely at one another. They asked me silently what I could do and I answered silently, nothing. I finally managed to get out a few half-strangulated words to the effect that he did not have to hit him, then looked inquiringly toward the patients for their reply. They too said they could do nothing, moved uncertainly, then milled about as the door into the single room closed.

I reported the assault to the proper authorities. It happened to have been the last day of work for the man with the fist. The other attendants did not deny that it had happened; "if she said so, it must have," but they could not corroborate the hitting because "we were very busy taking care of ourselves and the patient and could not notice everything."

This episode concerned me deeply; I discussed it with many persons in the hospital. Apparently people agreed that I had acted appropriately; they offered no alternative suggestions. Some, I think, thought I took it too seriously, which meant that I should have forgotten it, not reported it. It was only some time later that I suddenly realized what I should have done. I had the prerogative and indeed the responsibility simply to walk over to the group on the floor and to tell them to pick the patient up and to take him to a single room. This is the ordinary human response. Why had it not been mine?

In my defense, I thought of a past episode in another hospital. I was with a manic patient who had vomited in the dining room; we were on our way to the seclusion room and she had stopped for a drink from the water fountain and a moment to clean her face. She had asked for nothing from me but my presence and we were nearly half of the distance to the seclusion room. The nurse she had doused with water "because she poisoned my dinner" came angrily down the hall, her equanimity lost in the individual confrontation that could not be avoided in the deserted hallway. She took the patient by the arm; the patient moved away to wash the vomit off her face. The nurse pulled her back, no face washing. The patient pulled, went to the floor. Nurse began to drag patient down the hall, patient objecting— signalling to let her up to wash her face. I tried to explain what patient and I had been doing. Nurse told me to help her. I said I would help get the patient to the seclusion room, but that I would not drag her while she was able and willing to walk. So the three of us went along the hall: nurse dragging, patient objecting, I lamely tagging along. Nurse reported me for insubordination. The supervisor told me in effect I was a good kid but had a lot to learn. When I stood near tears as the attendant hit the patient with his fist, I wondered if I had learned what she meant. I had not learned what I wished that I might.

c. 1970

25

"The French Kiss and the Pinch"

ROBBIE SKEIST

The head nurse becomes angry when an orderly allows a young inmate to kiss him. As the boy himself remarks to the nurse, she would not have been so upset by heterosexual kiss, though inmates are officially allowed no sexual satisfaction of any kind.

TODAY'S CRISIS came when Lenny, a patient around 15 years old, gave me a French kiss. Just before, Michael—who was discharged from the Army when they caught him making love (not war) with another soldier—had smiled, hugged me, and given me a smack of a kiss on my cheek. I thought Lenny was about to do the same, but instead he went for my mouth.

His lips were wet. He put his tongue in and moved it around. It was a good kiss and I couldn't tell him to stop. Still, the head nurse was standing about seven feet away watching, quite surprised, so I couldn't respond. I stood there. He kissed me. After a while, maybe four or five seconds—delicious, anxiety-filled seconds—the nurse came running out and screamed, "Lenny! Stop that!" I think she pulled his arms from around me and scolded him. He asked if she would be as upset if he were kissing a woman. She muttered something about "You know the rules."

Three hours later, Mr. Waller, a licensed practical nurse, pulled me over and said he was going to have a "fatherly talk" with me. The head nurse told him to tell me she was upset that I had just stood there when Lenny kissed me. I told him I was stunned so I didn't react, which was misleading because I didn't explain how nice the stunning kiss was. Mr. Waller said if it happens again, I should push Lenny away and insist he stop.

At the end of his little lecture, Mr. Waller gave me a little pinch on the side of my stomach, gathering a roll of my fat between his large thumb and forefinger. It felt good.

c. 1970

26

"Hosprison"

JAN MARKS

Some doctors become addicted to self-prescribed drugs. Dr. Marks was one of them. Because his life was being disrupted by his dependency on the synthetic narcotic Demerol (a tradename for meperidine), Marks was sent to the federal mental hospital for drug addicts at Lexington, Kentucky.

Marks details the pervasive controls attendant-guards exercise over inmates—though the rules were not as strictly enforced by the time of his second stay two years later, when research volunteers were rewarded with days off rather than narcotics. He also gives an excellent description of the ward atmosphere.

Doctors Duffy and Litin report treating ten addicted physician-inmates in the Mayo Clinic inpatient psychiatric service, including one doctor addicted to Demerol.[1]

ABOUT A week after my admission, I and several other patients in the admitting ward were given grey prison-type uniforms to put on and escorted to skid row.

Skid row was actually only a subdivision of population; its purpose was apparently to give new patients an introduction to life at Lexington before they were assigned to permanent living quarters. Beyond the guard's room were a day room and two rows of wards called "drums," separated by a corridor. The drums in one row were racially segregated from those in the other. Between each two drums was a bathroom containing two washbowls, a commode and a shower. Semi-partitions separated the beds and bed-tables which were provided the three to seven men in each drum.

117

On our arrival, we new men were given the customary welcoming lecture by a guard official. The latter informed us that we were not in a hotel and that if we wanted to get along we had better obey regulations and not listen to what the other men told us.

Most of the rules seemed to concern inspection, which occurred once a week. Then floors had to be scrubbed, beds had to be made with rigid care, army-style, every article had to be in its place and every speck of dust had to be removed. Men who failed to pass inspection could expect extra work details. For "real wise guys" and repeated failures there were solitary cells. Lights went out every night at ten, and whoever dared open his mouth after that hour did so at the risk of punishment.

As I listened to the official speak, I knew—although I had physically left only one part of the hospital building for another—that I was now actually in a prison. No doctors, nurses or medical aides were anywhere in evidence. The khaki-clothed security guards (called "hacks") were in full control. The only way out of the area was screened off by a grill at the guard's room.

The single most overwhelming impression now was one of noise. I had never experienced anything like it. Out of the drums, and, especially, out of the day room, poured a continual torrent of raucousness from morning till night.

The day room was an enormous bleak space, empty except for four tables with chairs. Except for those sitting at or lying on the tables, and others standing at the windows the men inside were in perpetual motion, slapping each other's palms in greeting as they passed. No one seemed to be able to speak in a normal voice. There was an unending tumult of roaring laughter, shouted profanity, outbursts of anger and screaming. Only when one of the hacks happened to come through did the din subside, to resume as soon as he disappeared from view. There were frequent arguments among the card and domino players at the tables and there were sometimes fights. Chairs might then be used as weapons. They were heavy chairs, and it was possible to knock a man down by skidding a chair across the slick floor from one end of the room to another: this, in fact, was a favorite form of horseplay. I also saw men skidded across the floor and into the wall.

It was difficult in all the noise to hear what anyone was saying, but gradually I became aware that almost all of the talk centered on four topics: dope, crime, Cadillacs and women.

118

Especially dope. Many of the men were boisterous hoodlums who had no desire to abstain from narcotics and could hardly wait to pick up their old habits as soon as they left the hospital. They told one another incredible stories of the huge habits they had maintained. They knew, they averred, exactly where they were going to get their first shot after they were released—less than an hour's ride from the city of Lexington. They could, on the other hand, be brought low by being told, "Why, you're not even a real junkie!" This was a terrible charge, and the words always provoked an argument, if not a fight.

Almost as much as they boasted about their habits, they spoke magniloquently of the crimes they had committed to pay for them. They lied shamelessly and loudly—about the big jobs they had pulled, about their connections in the underworld and politics, and about their enormous wealth. It was impossible to believe them, and yet they described in fervid detail the custom-built Cadillacs they drove on the outside and talked of the scores of beautiful women who were only waiting for them to come back. The usual command of the guard before lights were turned out was "O.K., boys, park your Cadillacs!" My ears tingled for a long time in the unaccustomed silence . . . .

I had been wondering for some days about the patients who stood for long intervals before the windows of the day room. Every now and then they suddenly became animated and jerked their hands as in some sign language. Then I found out what they were up to. The windows faced a parking lot. Whenever nurses or women patients came into view the men at the windows tried to communicate with them. The practice was called "trembling" and was forbidden. It was punishable by long hours of washing floors and windows. Persistent tremblers were given solitary confinement.

At mealtimes the patients in skid row mingled freely with the others in population, for there were no separate dining facilities for the new men.

Before each meal the gate to skid row would be jammed with patients jostling to get out first. So many were let out at a time; then they might be held at a second gate. The dining rooms lay off both sides of a single corridor. Food was served cafeteria style and the rule was that one ate all that one took.

At my first dinner as a resident of skid row, I suffered an attack of cramps. I was seated at table, looking disgustedly at my tray. A guard ambled over and asked me why I wasn't eating. I replied that I couldn't eat, whipped out a cigarette and lit it. The man beside me kicked my foot in warning and I immediately stamped out my cigarette. Littering floors was tolerated no more than smoking, and when the guard had walked away my neighbor informed me that now I was "going to get it." However, he showed me how to dispose of the food I could not eat by cramming it into my coffee cup and covering it over with coffee from the coffee urn: coffee could be wasted. Thanks to his solicitude for a bumbling neophyte, nothing afterwards happened to me.

There were a few bright moments at Lexington. The hospital had a bank, in which the money taken from me at the entrance gate had been deposited in my name. I could increase my account by signing over postal money orders sent from the outside. Once a week patients were allowed to buy books of coupons worth one, two, five or ten dollars in merchandise at the commissary: fountain pens, writing paper, ice-cream, playing cards and, even, radios. Walking past the dining rooms to Central Control, one came to a flight of steps leading into the basement. Here was the recreation area, comprising a basketball gym, a weight lifting room, two rooms with pool tables and two bowling alleys. But it was rarely that I found any of these facilities uncrowded.

Most of the time I spent with the knowledge that I was in fact in prison and that the "cure" I was supposed to be taking was scarcely more than a hideous travesty. I was told in detail about the block of isolation cells and about the occasional smuggling in of narcotics from the outside. I was astounded to hear that patients who volunteered for experiments in the research unit were "paid off" in narcotics. This paradoxical practice of using narcotics as a reward in a hospital for narcotic addicts, rather than time off from sentences, better meals or more privileges, seemed something more than stupid; it was evil.

1955

27

"Mutual Fury"

DAVID CLARK

Superintendent Clark's tale of bureaucratic mismanagement illustrates how responsibility is shifted from one department to another in mental hospitals.

Former superintendent Walter Barton tells of a similar instance of buck-passing in a United States mental hospital: "Not an uncommon situation is illustrated by the following: A mischievous patient blocks up holes wherever he can find them; he wads up paper and stuffs it into keyholed, plugs key-operated light switches and floor drains, and stuffs his trousers into the toiled. The Maintenance Foreman, harassed by plumbing stoppages and electric repairs, complains to the Business Manager who requests help from the Superintendent; the Superintendent informs the Director of Nurses. The Director of Nurses tells the Nursing Supervisor, and the Supervisor instructs the Ward Nurse to exercise better control over her patients. The nurse asks the doctor for help with her problem patient. What happens? The patient often gets transferred to another ward."[1]

AT AN English mental hospital there was a cold spell just before Christmas. The elderly patients suffered considerable distress because there was not enough fuel to put on the fires. Accusations flew back and forth. The matron said that the engineer had mismanaged the coal supplies; the engineer said that the supplies officer had not ordered enough coal; the supplies officer said that the system of delivering coal had been changed and that the secretary had not told him it was not working; the secretary said that the matron failed to exercise adequate control of the use of fuel; Management

121

Committee members who saw the old ladies shivering said that the medical superintendent was at fault in allowing this to happen. Brief inquiry established that this had happened during several previous winters and that there was a history of troubles going back at least twenty years. The medical superintendent decided that he must involve himself.

He called a meeting of all the officers and after a period of ventilation of accusations and mutual fury they began to try to find out what did happen. It soon emerged that no officer accepted responsibility, and no one really knew what was happening. During the war the engineer had been in charge of all coal and its allocation, but when rationing ceased he no longer felt himself responsible; with the appointment of a supplies officer, the secretary did not feel himself responsible; since the supplies officer had a distant office he expected that someone closer would see to it, and so on. Investigation showed that house coal was delivered from the colliery by lorry at intervals depending on the convenience of the supplier; that the coal was put in an open dump and later moved into small dumps near the wards by a ward orderly and a gang of patients with wheelbarrows. These dumps were also open and the ward staff sent patients to get as much coal as they could whenever they felt the need. There was no check of the amounts moved; the orderly just did his best to keep everyone happy. If the weather changed unexpectedly, everyone went cold.

It took five months of meetings, investigations, and checks, and several meetings with the chairman of the Management Committee, before the system of ordering was changed and the responsibilities of the various officers delineated. During this period the medical superintendent acted as chairman of the *ad hoc* committees, and he was constantly concerned with coal, its prices and qualities, until methods of supply and control had been worked out. By that time the winter was over, but in following winters supplies flowed well. The medical superintendent never again concerned himself with details of coal.

c. 1955

28

"Condemned Dreams"

CARL SOLOMON

Solomon reports that he entered New York Psychiatric Institute after a turbulent period during which, he reports, he was guilty of "hurling refuse at a lecturer." He reputedly threw potato salad at a City College lecturer on dadaism, but he has corrected this version: "It was thrown at an off-campus Brooklyn College lecturer on Mallarmè who had humiliated me for no cause at a party several years earlier".[1] At the New York Psychiatric Institute he met inmate Allen Ginsberg, then at the end of a short stay, who later dedicated "Howl" to Solomon. The poem has the line, "Carl Solomon! I'm with you in Rockland," though Solomon was actually transferred to Pilgrim State Hospital.

Here Solomon wryly describes a masquerade ball that is meant to be therapeutic.

THE PSYCHIATRIC ineptitude of the official lower echelons became incredible when, one week before Halloween, it was announced to the patients that a masquerade ball would be held on the appropriate date, the attendance was to be mandatory, and that a prize would be given to the patient wearing the "best" costume. Whereupon, the patients, among whom there was a high spirit of competition, threw themselves precipitously into the work of creating what, for each, promised to be the most striking disguise. The work of sewing, tearing, dyeing, etc., was done in Occupational Therapy, where, at the disposal of all, were an infinite variety of paints, gadgets, and fabrics. Supervising all this furious activity was a pedagogic harpy, who had been assigned as Occupational Therapist to see that we

123

didn't destroy any of the implements in the shop (she tried to persuade me to attend the masquerade made up as a dog). Furiously we labored, competing with one another even in regard to speed of accomplishment, fashioning disguised phalluses, swords, spears, scars for our faces, enormous cysts for our heads. When Halloween Night arrived, we were led, dazed and semi-amnesiac, into the small gymnasium that served as a dance floor. Insidious tensions intruded themselves as the time for the awarding of the prize approached. Finally, the Social Therapists seated themselves in the center of the polished floor and ordered us to parade past them in a great circle; one of the nurses sat at the piano and played a march; to the strains of the music, we stepped forward to present our respective embodied idealizations to the judges. There were several Hamlets, a Lear, a grotesque Mr. Hyde, a doctor; there were many cases of transvestism; a young man obsessed with the idea that he was an inanimate object had come as an electric-lamp, brightly-lit, complete with shade; a boy who had filled his head to the point of bursting with baseball lore had come as a "Brooklyn Bum," in derby and tatters. Suddenly, the music stopped; the judges had chosen a winner, rejecting the others; we never learned who the winner had been, so chaotic was the scene that followed. There was a groan of deep torment from the entire group (each feeling that his dream had been condemned). Phantasmal shapes flung themselves about in despair. The nurses and Social Therapists spent the next hour in consoling the losers.

1959

29

"I Don't Believe in Mental Torture"

MILTON ROKEACH

Leon was one of three men at Ypsilanti State Hospital, Michigan, who thought themselves Christ. He had also dubbed himself, Dr. Dung, psychiatrist, and claimed that a "Madame Yeti Woman" was both his wife and God. To counter these beliefs, social psychologist Rokeach had letters written to Leon signed Madame Yeti Woman. When, after eight weeks, Leon began to reject the letters, Rokeach tried to restore "Madame Dung's" supposedly beneficial influence. He has an "uncle," who Leon delusively believes exists, call with a reinforcing message.

In a parallel instance of fraud, the superintendent of a Hungarian mental hospital recalls how he brought an obstreperous inmate to heel: "I re-conquered Leslie with a pious—or impious—fraud. He had someone write a card . . . to the Head Doctor of Lipotmezo, in which he asked to be taken back. I did not forward the card but wrote an answer myself in the name of the Head Doctor: 'Dear Leslie, There was a lot of trouble with you here, too; you were always impertinent and did not work . . . Stay put where you are, and try to behave yourself . . . ' When the answer was read to Leslie, he blushed, then went white, and the effect was stunning. I don't dare repeat the curse he flung at that innocent Head Doctor—may she forgive me. But then he became calm, diligent and ambitious, and always tried to prove what a good boy he was . . . And he really was a good boy."[1]

LATER IN the evening, after our attempt to show Leon that Dr. Broadhurst [a resident psychiatrist] had nothing to do with the letters, an aide informs him that there is a person-to-person long-

125

distance call for Dr. R. I. Dung. Leon replies that he is busy and doesn't want to be bothered. The aide tells him that it is a man on the other end of the phone. Leon asks who it is. The aide replies that he did not give his name, whereupon Leon comes to the office and picks up the phone. The voice at the other end identifies itself as that of his Uncle George Bernard Brown, and goes on to say that he has been touch with Madame Dung, that they are both working for his redemption and that Leon must not say that Madame Dung, who is also God, is insane or negative. Leon listens, apparently with much interest. Then suddenly he interrupts: "Sir, excuse me, sir, your voice doesn't sound like my uncle. Good-bye sir!" And he hangs up and returns to the sitting room.

About a quarter of an hour later, the aide goes to the room where Leon, as before the call, is praying on his knees. When the aide inquires about the call, Leon replies: "Don't bother me, sir. The call was from someone at the other end of the extension. This was done through the switchboard. I don't believe in mental torture, sir. What he said doesn't matter, sir. Now would you leave me alone, sir? Thank you for helping me, sir."

It was now clear that we had failed in our last-ditch effort to reinstate Madame Yeti Woman as a positive authority and that, moreover, our effort had only succeeded in making Leon extremely upset. The time had now clearly come to terminate any further experimental attempts in this direction.

1959

30

"Stupid Girl. Stupid Girl. Scrub. Scrub. Scrub."

D. L. STANNARD

Sociology doctoral student Stannard worked for eighteen months as an attendant on the locked acute ward of the psychiatric service of a private hospital in California.

He divides ward personnel into a "sociostaff," which focuses on social processes. The "harassment therapy" in which the psychostaff indulges is supposed to bring out inmates' inward-turned anger at the controlled environment. The harassment can stimulate sadomasochistic feelings, however, and staff members do not deal with these powerful emotions that the game-playing arouses in themselves, as well as in the inmates. Further, the harassment functions as punishment, therapeutic intention notwithstanding.

The newsletter of the American Association for the Abolition of Involuntary Hospitalization, *The Abolitionist,* reports in its Summer, 1971, issue: "Therapeutic beatings allegedly caused the death of one patient and back injuries to another, according to accounts in Phoenix, Arizona, newspapers. Two psychiatrists acting as community mental health consultants had applied a 'radical treatment' called Rage Reduction Therapy. 'It consists of physical action directed at passive-aggressive patients as treatment for their condition and involves a range of attacks from tickling to heavy physical blows.'" *The Abolitionist* reports another example of the danger of harassment therapy in its August 1972 issue: "A San Jose (Cal.) jury awarded $170,000 damages to a young woman who had undergone thirteen hours of 'rage reduction therapy,' in which she claimed to have suffered near-fatal kidney damage, severe bodily bruises, and a lacerated mouth."

JANE, A young patient on the ward, was tearfully scrubbing the small floor in the shower room. On the floor were powdery detergent flakes, mixed with water in some spots, dry and caked elsewhere. She sat on her heels, hunched over her task. She rubbed the white mess in front of her with a toothbrush. Even in such a tiny room, using such a small instrument to "clean" the floor looked absurd.

In the small room with her were two female psychiatric technicians. One was quite large, and seemed to be in charge. The other stood in the doorway, observing the scene; she couldn't have squeezed all the way into the small room, probably no larger than 3 by 5 feet, had she wanted to.

The large tech straddled Jane, and shouted directions at her. She demanded that the girl "clean up this mess" and added: "Stupid girl, stupid girl, Goddamn stupid girl." Jane went on scrubbing, went on crying.

The large tech turned to her co-worker, who was assisting her, and announced: "This girl isn't working hard enough. I'm going to get something that will really make her work."

The big tech then left the room; the second in command took over directing the patient. "Stupid girl. Stupid girl. Scrub. Scrub. Scrub."

The smaller tech pushed over a pail of water that was sitting in the small room. The dirty contents flowed all over the floor, sloshing up against Jane's kneeling legs and mixing together the various wet and dry clumps of powder that covered the floor. The small tile that Jane had been scrubbing clean for the last half hour was suddenly covered with a gooey mess of soap suds and dirty water. She wept louder, but said nothing.

The bigger tech returned. She screamed: "Look at that mess! Look at that mess. You dumb girl, just look at that mess." She then proceeded to throw bright colored paint, the contents of plastic cups used by the patients for finger-painting projects, on to the floor. The yellows and blues mixed with the soap and dirty water, and turned into a sickening green. The reds and oranges looked brown after sloshing on the floor for a few minutes.

Jane and both techs were speckled with colorful dots of the finger paints; dust from the soap powder covered everything and everyone in the room. Jane cried, but continued to scrub the tile with her toothbrush.

And on another day I noted:

Patient Anne was started on harassment therapy. She was given

128

the task of making and remaking her bed (a staff member tearing the bed apart every time she completed the job). Anne complied, but only after informing the staff that she "could take it," since she was going home in two days anyway.

This incident strained intra-staff relationships even more than usual. The patient was quite right in saying she was going home in two days. She was a voluntary patient, and the previous day she had given the 72-hour notice that was supposedly required when a patient wanted to leave against medical advice. Since harassment therapy is usually a drawn-out process, requiring weeks or even months to complete a program, the staff was not only divided over the philosophy behind the techique, but also over its usage in this particular case.

The psychostaff generally agreed that Anne was "quite sick," and felt that perhaps she would recognize her need for hospitalization as she experienced the emotional stress and strain brought on by the harassment program; also, since Anne was deemed to be "fragile," she might explode, and "act out" homicidally or suicidally; the staff could then "document" her "crazy" behavior, and hopefully she would then be committed for "needed" psychiatric care.

c. 1971

31

"Vegetables Don't Cry"

EILEEN WALKENSTEIN

Psychiatrist Walkenstein describes the ghoulish lobotomy that a neurosurgeon performed on a young black man who had recently been hospitalized. The 1950s heyday of lobotomies is past, but some psychiatrists and neurosurgeons are still performing psychosurgery.

YES, SADISM in medicine and neurosurgery and psychiatry is, alas, still rearing its ugly head and destroying human heads in its wake.

My own introduction to modern neurosurgery occurred in my second or third year in medical school—occurred, literally, in one fell swoop, cutting its way into my own brain and leaving the scar even now, some twenty years later.

I refer to the transorbital lobotomy, otherwise known as the ice pick operation. Techniques of this wounding were perfected to such a degree that all that was required was an ice pick-like instrument—no sutures, no bandages—internal bleeding and destruction of nerve pathways and irrevocable death of brain cells with just a thrust of the ice pick . . . and all that's evident on the outside are two black eyes— that clear up in time—and memory loss—that doesn't clear up so well . . . and a state of docile vegetation—that goes on forever. With a flick of the wrist the animal gets changed into a plant—modern alchemy!

My medical school class was invited to see a demonstration of such a transorbital lobotomy, one of the several type of lobotomies. The neurosurgeon, on the staff of a university medical school, stood before the class strutting in a sedate, self-important manner. I remember how good looking and smooth he appeared, a typical Hollywood symbol of the handsome doctor whose patients go ga-ga over him . . . and how entirely devoid of character he was. He was meticulously groomed, hair perfectly in place, skin very white and smooth shaven—a perfect, successful representative of White Anglo-Saxon America. He wore a suit and tie and looked as if he were addressing a businessmen's luncheon meeting of the Kiwanis Club. After some introductory remarks he opened the door and the nurse and orderly pushed a stretcher into the room. Walking in with them was an attractive young black man, eighteen years old, looking frightened and bewildered. The neurosurgeon paid no attention to him but continued discussing with us how the operation would be conducted, and he seemed proud of the fact that they didn't even need anesthesia for the operation—that knocking the patient out with "a couple of electric shock treatments would be adequate anesthetization." (I guess when you're contemplating slashing up the brain substance, a little cell damage more or less is not too relevant.)

The young black man in wrinkled hospital garb stood cowering in the corner in sharp contrast with the urbane, smooth, self-possessed, polished physician. Finally the doctor turned to the patient, mentioned his diagnosis . . . Schizophrenic Reaction . . . and that he was a recent hospital admission . . . and told him to get up on the stretcher. The young man backed up, his shoulders hunched like a scared cat being attacked by a growling bulldog, his eyes darting this way and that in a futile attempt to seek some way of escape from the inevitable. The nurse and orderly then held his arms, brought him to the stretcher, and somehow managed to get him to lie down on it, shackling his wrists and ankles. The doctor applied the electrodes to the young man's temples, the current was turned on, and the young man's body jerked convulsively for several seconds. The doctor said smoothly, as though nothing had just happened, that he thought he'd give another dose of electric current to be sure he's knocked out completely. Again the current was turned on, again the captured victim was convulsively responding with his entire body to the electricity searing his brain cells.

(This patient—if he were not poor, not black, not welfare-experimental-animal material—what treatment would then have been meted out to him? . . . need one ask such an obvious question? What treatment for this young black man had he been in the doctor's own family, for instance? *This is the criterion.* If you treat me, no matter who I am, in any way different from the way you would treat your family members and colleagues and peers, then you don't deserve to be in a service profession—get out and get into business! In business you treat everyone with equal contempt, independent of their blood relationship to you—business is business. So get out of the service and helping professions, you doctors, educators, priests, et al. who would dehumanize us—get into the material world— unadulteratedly corrupt—and practice your corruptions on my pocketbook but not on my flesh, my intellect, my spirit!)

I find it very difficult to get back and face that patient who has just had his second electroconvulsive assault. Since leaving him there I have just now busied myself with phone calls, checking my calendar, eating a homemade milk-and-honey popsicle, and just plain vacating my mind and floating for a while. The subsequent scene is so horrible not only in itself but in all its ramifications that I've been avoiding delving in and confronting it.

Well, back again—that patient was, after the second electric shock, completely limp and "anesthetized." (I have never, neither before nor since that incident, heard of using electricity for anesthesia!) The surgeon then took an instrument *from his pocket* in a pointedly and overly nonchalant manner and showed the ice-pick-like tool to the class. He then lifted one eyelid of the patient's and stuck the pick up— he made a point of showing that he was having some trouble getting the pick through the skull and into the brain at the first try and he grimaced at the class and said something about the "thickness of the boy's skull." A few of the more obvious racists in the class gave him his anticipated reply by snickering—some of the students, already uncomfortable, had their discomfort increased at this remark. After the pick penetrated the skull, he flicked his wrist back and forth with the pick slashing into the brain substance, severing forever, in an instant, those connections that nature had labored to achieve over millions of years. The Brain-Killer, named Neurosurgeon, repeated the ceremony via the patient's other eye socket.

I was not the only one who gasped at the outrage I had just witnessed. One girl, Dottie, her head probably full of the sterile operative techniques with sterilization of instruments we'd been taught to observe prior to and during the operation, raised her hand and asked about using an unsterilized instrument, to which the surgeon retorted with a pretty-boy smile: "Well, I didn't wipe it on my bootstrap."

"VEGETABLES DON'T CRY"

Who was there to raise the bigger question—by what right had this surgeon, knowing almost nothing about the patient except that he was black, eighteen, on welfare, and a new hospital admission, butchered this young man's brain for the education of a class of young doctors-to-be? *Who were all those responsible for all the steps required to bring that patient's brain in contact with that butcher's ice pick?*

The show was over—the showman strutted in front of the room, titillated at his own performance—at the suave, nonchalant way he imposed a gruesome spectacle on a class of horrified doctors-to-be.

The young man, never to be whole again, lying stretched out before us, was wheeled out of the room, out of most of our lives. He will always be part of mine—seared forever in my brain, in my guts.

May, as Goethe promised, the pain be halved now that I've shared it with you . . . may the load of it be lighter for me. It will never be lighter for that young man—he is beyond weights and measures—beyond the pain of butcheries—*vegetables don't cry.*

c. 1949

133

32

"Patient Government"

JANE FRY

A pre-operative transsexual born male, Fry had long since been impressed with the idea that he was a "mental case." When his wife's pregnancy touched off an emotional crisis in him, he entered a Veterans Administration Hospital psychiatric ward.

In his account, Fry brings across the inmate's lack of real power to deal meaningfully with even the trivial issues discussed in patient government.

Mental hospital accounts mirror each other with startling fidelity. Anne Barry[1] reports a discussion of cigarette-stealing at a ward meeting. One woman says, "There's a problem with stealing. Somebody steals cigarettes all the time." Another inmate adds, "And I know who it is. Everybody know who it is, but nobody make her stop."

A sanctimonious clinician mollifies according to formula: "I don't think we should accuse anyone, because so far as I know, no one has caught this person in the act of stealing. But if we talk about it in general, that person will know how we all feel about it, and will know that she has to stop."

THE PATIENTS have this patients' government, which is kind of a joke. I used it a couple of times, and so did some of the other patients, but mostly we would joke about it. This was especially true of the veterans coming back from Vietnam. They were the ones who started calling it "student" government. At the VA patient government is like milieu therapy—someone's pipedream that doesn't work in practice.

134

It looks good on paper, and that's about all; it doesn't do anybody any good. They can't make any decisions. What they can do is ask the staff to do something, but the staff makes the decision. Sometimes people who had grievances against each other took them to it. What happens is that they discuss it and then come up with a decision, and then the staff carries it out. The patient could have just as easily gone to the staff in the first place and asked for the same thing—in 99 percent of the cases they would have decided the same way.

The patient government make people more dependent on those on the ward instead of directly doing something about what's bothering them. Instead of patient government and milieu therapy helping people, it only helps them relate to each other and forget about the outside, which is the reverse of what it is supposed to be.

Everyone on the ward was supposed to serve on the committee. I was on the Grievance Committee, which was basically one guy bitching about another. It is supposed to be a logical way of one patient airing his grievances against another. So, instead of two patients talking it out to each other, they go running to the Grievance Committee which keeps them from having it out with each other. Say, someone steals cigarettes, or one patient is a compulsive thief. One thing you learn right off in the hospital, by the way, is to keep your belongings on you at all times. He steals from one patient who gets pissed off and complains to the Grievance Committee. On the Grievance Committee are four patients and one doctor. The staff already knew the guy is a compulsive thief and the guy knew he was doing it, and it had already been kind of settled by the attendants— they told everybody to keep their cigarettes put away. So the Grievance Committee met on it and sent its recommendation to Patient Government, which was read at the meeting. It went something like, "A person who we shall not name" (it was asinine because everybody knew who we were talking about) has been stealing cigarettes." Well, the thing went on, and ended up with recommendations that everybody keep their cigarettes to themselves, which everybody knew in the first place. It made you feel like a fool. You felt that you were being made fun of doing all that for nothing.

c. 1969

33

"Back Ward"

MARSHALL EDELSON

A psychiatric resident at Shepherd and Enoch Pratt Hospital in Maryland rouses half of the most disturbed male ward by making a simple request. The incident suggests that inmates' actions are often a direct response to the way they are treated.

MY FIRST experience with the therapeutic community was as a first-year resident in psychiatry in the mid-fifties. My wife and I lived on the grounds of the hospital. I woke up one morning to find the hospital buried in snow, no other physician able to get in to work, and myself in charge. I decided to try to shovel our way out of isolation. For some reason—I can't quite remember my state of mind at the time—I decided to go to the most disturbed closed male unit and ask the patients there to help shovel snow. With the help of the maintenance department I collected a large number of shovels, went to the unit, and faced an aggregate of catatonic and hebephrenic patients, among others, in various states of agitation, preoccupation, and immobility. I explained as best I could the dilemma the hospital was in, and asked for volunteers to help shovel the snow. As I remember, about ten or twelve out of the twenty volunteered, put on their hats and coats, and marched from the hall. Ordinarily, these patients never left the hall without maximum nursing coverage; we only had a relatively small number of personnel that day available to join us. We shoveled snow most of the morning. Afterwards, we went to the kitchen together, and had hot chocolate and a fairly pleasant time without difficulties; it would have been hard to distinguish these

136

patients from others on open units. Then we returned to the disturbed closed male unit; the patients took off their hats and coats and immediately resumed their catatonia and hebephrenia.

This has always been a dramatic example to me of an idea that we take for granted as a truism but the implications of which perhaps we do not consider fully: that the behavior of patients, in fact the behavior of all persons, is determined by the situation in which they find themselves as well as (and not only) by relatively enduring aspects of the personality system. This idea underlies any notion of therapeutic community or therapeutic milieu.

1957

34

"Schizophrenia Chronic Undifferentiated Type"

JACKIE DAYMOON

An attendant caring for physically sick old people at a California mental hospital sees humans treated like objects.

I WAS a student technician at Napa State Hospital in 1975. This hospital has been called "a warehouse" for humans, but that term is much too kind.

The first assignment we had on the psych ward was on the medical-surgical floor. When we walked in there what we saw was rows of big cribs where old women were lying in them in the fetal position, in diapers, moaning, groaning. Most of them had contractures. Their muscles, their arms, legs, hands had not been exercised. Our job was to go in there and feed them and transfer them to a gurney, wheel them down the hall, put them in a bath tub and wash them up each day. And all this time the staff did not talk to these people. They would occasionally talk about them or joke about them, but, these old people were just not spoken to and so, through the years, they had stopped speaking.

After we would give them a bath they would be sat up in a chair, tied in with sheets. Their shoulders and legs would be tied on to the chair so that they would not fall out. They would sit in this room, sometimes it was a four bedroom. The staff letting them sit up for a couple of hours and then dump them back into bed, never speaking to them. And, these people who could not move or who had stopped moving and talking, were not even taken out into the day room. They never heard a radio. They never saw a television. They never saw people coming and going. They just saw this grey-green room, day-in and day-out, day-in and day-out.

By the way, their feeding budget up there was $1.51 a day per person. So they have gotten very little meat and absolutely no raw vegetables, no salad. I asked about that and they (the staff) told me, "Well, it is just too much trouble. It wasn't convenient." They mostly got mush and devitalized food, white bread, cream of wheat, a lot of dishes with noodles (white noodles), starchy, lifeless food. They also got scrambled eggs when they were lucky, made out of powdered egg mix. And these chronic people who were in their beds and who did not talk and who could not protest anymore, I was taught how to feed them quickly so that I could get on with my other work. We would take the powdered scrambled eggs and mash them up with coffee and suck it up into a plastic syringe and go through, pry their teeth open and just squirt it down. We had to do it fast since we had so many people to feed. The patients would be gulping it as fast as they could and sometimes choking and spitting it out.

There was one woman, I was assigned to her, her name was Marie and she didn't speak at all. They were all called SCUT, Schizophrenia Chronic Undifferentiated Type. So, I had made it my project to get her to talk within the 6 weeks I was there. I just talked to her constantly while I made her bed, while I washed her, while I changed her clothes and combed her hair. I talked to her constantly and after a certain time she began to just watch me, follow me around the bed with her eyes which is more than she had done before. People thought I was pretty nutty for trying to talk to this woman who was just a vegetable. So, as the weeks went on and I kept telling her, "Oh Marie, I won't give up on you. I know you can talk. I know you can hear me," and I tried speaking a little Spanish now and then as she looked like she might have spoken Spanish; finally she started to move her arms. I found a little stuffed animal and gave it to her. She seemed to like that. That was the first response I had gotten from her. She would reach out for the stuffed animal and I would give it to her and she would hold on to it. I would come in and start talking and talking and start singing to her. She finally started to move around, just to move her head from side to side and to move her arms a little bit. She would reach out with this little stuffed animal and touch me repeatedly, just kind of bump me very gently with this as if she was trying to connect or just making contact. Well the nurse, when they saw her starting to move a little bit, told me that I was upsetting her and making her nervous. So I was not allowed to do it anymore.

1975

35

"Vertical Extraction"

DAVID VAIL

Vail was innovatively reforming the Minnesota state mental hospital system as its chief medical officer when he suddenly died in 1971. Here he introduces a tale of institutionalization with these words: "In this poignant description, a hospital employee shows how years of institutional life can flatten a person and cause him to forget simple skills that for most of us are taken for granted. The author stressed the institutional lack of opportunity for making decisions." Vail's informant illustrates how very dependent on the hospital the inmate can become.

I WENT to get a patient from R. ward (admission 1933 at age nineteen with diagnosis of hebephrenic schizophrenia, following sudden onset: as of 1954 diagnosis is mild mental deficiency-familial . . . hence, a potential candidate for a mental retardation commitment). When we reached an exit door (the front door is open, but this door leads down to an office area) I held out the key and said, "Jane, would you like to unlock the door?" She said that she would and took the keys. I have done this before and believe me it is a painful experience to watch a human being wrestle with what is a simple automatic task for most people. When asked if she wanted to lock the door, she agreed, and again the struggle with making the full turn and the necessary vertical extraction. But, how often has Jane used a key in the past thirty-four years? Then, you ask yourself, "How often has Jane dialed a telephone number, baked a cake, hammered a nail, changed a diaper, planted a seed, picked a chicken, rowed a boat, drawn a bath, changed a light bulb, opened a can . . . ad infinitum?"

140

"VERTICAL EXTRACTION"

What has she done for thirty-four years? She has been herded sheep-like from one building to another, and on the hour told when to eat (food chosen by others), what to wear (clothing selected by others), when to take a walk and where, when to wash, when to take a pill, when to go to church and where, when to see a movie or a television program (chosen by others), when to go to work and where . . . and so on in every sphere of her existence!

When the interview was over, I asked Jane if she would like to stop off at the store for a candy bar. I asked if she knew where the store was located . . . she said "somewhere in the Main Building." Imagine in this geographically limited "cage" of hers she did not know exactly where the only store on the grounds is located . . . she has probably never been there.

In the store I said, "What kind of candy bar would you like? She said, "Any old kind." I said, "You might as well choose, pick out a couple." She quickly said, "A Snickers and a Hershey." She chose, but here again insidiously embedded in her life was another piece of directed behavior . . . *I told her to choose!*

So what is the purpose of this odd letter? Jane has an official I.Q. of 68, but when you ask her who Longfellow was, she says, "an author," she tells you the average American woman is "sixty-three inches tall" and she knows the definition of words such as *domestic, excavate* and *chemist.* I passed her a woman's magazine and selected a paragraph—she reads well, especially considering that she says she has seldom done any reading in the past thirty-four years. Is she mentally retarded (sixty-nine or below)?

When I passed Jane a pencil with which to sign her name she held it three inches from the point. She says that she never writes anymore.

When we got back to the ward, I sat down with her. To try for some brevity, I shall just say in summary that she spoke well and logically and effectively. When asked if she would like to do something to improve her way of life she smiled (probably hebephrenically) while tears rolled down her cheeks and she said, "I tried the beauty shop but it was too hard. I asked for another job but there weren't any more so I just sat down."

Granted that premorbidly Jane was not a Rhodes scholar . . . *But,* are we not seeing the results of a more-insidious-than-we-realize sensory deprivation, that of being denied nearly all human choice, even of the simplest kind?

1966

141

36

"Rebirth in a Therapeutic Community"

LEWIS KILLIAN

Sociology professor Killian finds his stay on a psychiatric unit most helpful.

Some would argue that his generally excellent life adjustment made him immune to the negative effects of hospitalization. Head doctor Sanford Bloomberg does admit in a discussion of Killian's experience that persons "with less personality strength . . . may very well fall into the category of psychiatric victims."

IT WAS a cold, rainy, gray Saturday afternoon but the gloom of the day could not possibly mirror the despondency which filled my whole being. There I sat, a 53-year-old man, happily married, professionally successful, financially affluent, crying like a lost child as I clenched and unclenched my fists. The psychiatrist, whom I had met only 10 minutes earlier, had just said, bluntly and finally, "I could prescribe more medicine for you, but I don't think that would help you get better. You need to get in another environment for a few days. There is a bed available this afternoon in the hospital I recommend."

Here was the verdict I had been secretly dreading for months: hospitalization. Willpower, vacations, tranquilizers, antidepressants, sporadic therapy—none had been able to stop my descent into uncontrollable depression. I had begun to dread what loomed ever larger as the only alternatives—a complete breakdown and hospitalization, or suicide.

In spite of years of study of social psychology, all my professional sophistication vanished now. "Insane" was only the worst of the frightening words that flashed through my disordered mind. "Institutionalized," "psychiatric ward," "mentally ill," "deviant" are only a few of the others that I can remember. Not only did I know that, in terms of what we sociologists call "labeling theory," my friends would hereafter perceive me differently; I was already experiencing the pain of a new self-definition. Just the day before I had gotten my driver's license renewed. One of the questions on the application had been, "Have you ever been hospitalized for mental illness?" Never again would I be able to answer "No" to this question. The realization was devastating.

At last, in anguish and desperation, I forced the words from my dry, constricted throat—"Yes, God damn it, I'll go!" Within a few minutes my wife was driving me to a hospital in a nearby town where I would become a patient in a "therapeutic community"—what I thought then was a euphemism for the psychiatric ward. I would have to learn for myself that the term was more than a sugar-coated label. Now, on the way to the hospital, I was still reacting to visions of the "snake pit." I cried out to my wife, "Oh, my God, they'll give me shock treatment." I could visualize myself in a strait-jacket, or immersed in a tub of water for hydrotherapy. At the same time, I worried about the cost of the treatment, how many days of sick leave I had accumulated at my university, what would be done about my class and my administrative responsibilities, how my poor wife would get along in a lonely house—every concern that had ever crossed my mind now raced through it in a parade of problems about which I could do absolutely nothing.

I remember my admission to the hospital only in fragments. My recollection leaps in one bound from the hospital parking lot to the scene at the side of the bed which was to be mine for—I did not know how long. Weeping again, I kissed my wife goodbye and heard the appalling words, "No visitors for 72 hours," and then I was alone among strangers. I didn't care: I wanted to be alone, to lapse into the bliss of unconsciousness. But immediately the therapeutic community began to break through my shell. "Have you eaten supper, Lewis?" "We all use first names here—patients and staff; I'm Helen, I'm a nurse." "We ordered the house supper for you in case you hadn't eaten." "You'll be in this room by yourself tonight—your roommate is home on LOA [leave of absence] and will be back tomorrow."

I stumbled out of the room to the food cart and, with someone's assistance, pulled out a tray of food which already had my name on it. The food held no appeal for me; for several days nothing in life had interested me—even eating, usually one of my greatest pleasures. I forced myself to eat, and I began to meet my fellow patients who were just finishing their supper in the small dining room. At this point, though, I still thought of them as "fellow inmates," not "patients."

Some of them seemed to confirm this stereotype, reinforcing my feeling, "Is this where I belong now—among a bunch of nuts?" One was a college boy still suffering from the effects of numerous trips on LSD. He looked and acted strange and disturbed; I was a little frightened by his behavior.

Other patients didn't live up to my fevered expectations at all. They seemed so "normal" that I wondered if they really were patients. After all, in this community staff and patients dressed alike. Apparently I looked the part of a patient to them, however! My depression must have shown in my face, my speech, and my posture. One motherly-looking older woman said to me, as she helped me get some instant coffee, "We understand—we've all been there ourselves." I found a little comfort in this. She seemed to be saying to me that I could come out of my shell, "let it all hang out," if I wished, without fear as to how my companions would react. Sometime later—I'm not sure when—I found myself weeping again and felt secure enough to say to the other people in the room, "I hope it's all right here to cry if you feel like it—I can't help it." Then and later I was able to learn that it was indeed all right. This was a community where pent-up feelings were supposed to be expressed, not stored up.

That night I began to get acquainted with the staff and with the culture of the community. Somewhere along the line, a nurse took my temperature; I think she checked my blood pressure, too. We inventoried everything I had brought into the hospital. I was required to give my keys to the nurse for safekeeping because the small knife on my key chain constituted a "sharp" in the lingo of the ward, and all sharps had to be kept behind the nurses' station. I was reminded by this that I really was suspect—I did not just imagine that I was in a somewhat abnormal state. I could accept this, though, for I wasn't sure that I might not harm myself. After I went to bed that night it reassured rather than disturbed me to realize that an attendant looked in on me every hour throughout the night.

Two memorable events stick with me from that first evening. One

144

patient, a young man with long hair, asked me if I'd like to play ping-pong. Later, a very nervous, fidgety woman to whom I had spoken earlier asked me if I would sit down and let her talk to me about her nervousness. In both cases I said and acted "Yes" against all my inclinations. I was miserable; I didn't really want to do anything but go home, but that was one thing I knew I shouldn't do. Mustering what little willpower I still had, I told myself that it would help me and, perhaps, others if I stopped nursing my misery and tried to think of other people. These brief episodes of interaction, forced as they were, did make me feel as if I were coming back to life a little.

With the aid of a sleeping pill plus my desperate need to escape from the treadmill of waking thought, I fell into a deep sleep on my strange couch. About 6:30 the next morning, though, I awakened to the familiar hell of my first encounter with the day. For weeks I had been awakening every morning with a sick, empty feeling, with a dread of the long hours before I could crawl back in bed. How could I endure yet another day when life seemed so meaningless, so tasteless, that there was nothing I looked forward to doing? This day was the worst yet: I was still the captive of my depression, and I realized where I was. What would I do with myself all day, confined within this tiny hospital ward? Would I ever get well again, or was this just the first of an endless succession of empty days? I writhed under the covers; I groaned; I crouched in a fetal position; I pounded my fists on the pillow. Finally, I turned on the light and picked up a book to try to read. Miraculously, I quickly fell asleep again, with the book fallen on my chest. I awakened again at 8 o'clock to the somewhat peremptory words of a nurse, "Wake up, Lewis; it's time for your medication." I opened my eyes to see a beautiful young woman standing at the foot of my bed. For the first time I felt a spark of interest in something; apparently I was not so insensitive to the world that I could not still enjoy girl-watching! I know it sounds sexist in this day of Women's Lib, but the procession of pretty and young nurses and nurse's aides who succeeded each other on the different shifts in the ward were sex symbols to me before I began to perceive them as competent young professionals.

My initial reaction to the patients was essentially one of resignation to the fact that for an indefinite time my lot was cast with a heterogeneous collection of individuals, none of whom I would have chosen as associates "on the outside." If I chose to act the snob, to resist incorporation into the community, the hospital would be a terribly lonely place for me. My powers of concentration were so limited at this point that I could not read or watch television for more than a few minutes. In addition, I had enough insight to know that even if I could enjoy these solitary, escapist activities, to do so would only delay the date of my discharge. Hence I forced myself to enter as vigorously as I could into the life of the community, from listening sympathetically to the problems of my fellow-sufferers to playing ping-pong with a 14-year-old boy.

My relationship with members of the staff posed a more complex problem, particularly at the start. Because of my professional background, my first reaction was to identify with them as fellow psychologists rather than with the patients. This created difficulties, for the great majority of the staff members were much younger than I was, some of them young enough to be my children. So I felt at first that while we might be fellow professionals, they were not even my peers. Subtly but quickly it was brought home to me by their actions that this definition of the status system of the community was not acceptable. Patients and staff constituted two separate castes; power lay with the staff. Within the patient caste, status differences were vague, informal, and minimal, based on such things as how long a patient had been on the ward, what privileges he enjoyed, how well he behaved, and what progress he seemed to have made toward the goal of discharge. The hierarchy within the staff was explicit and formal, manifest in some instances by name tags with titles on them. At the bottom of the hierarchy were the nurse's aides, male as well as female. Above them were the nurses, then the therapists, and at the apex of the power structure, "Doctor B," the psychiatrist to whom all requests and recommendations went for final decision. While he was seen infrequently, reminders of his power were ever-present. A frequently asked question was, "Has Dr. B been in today?," for a patient requesting new privileges could not know for certain that they had been granted until after his review.

The power vested in the staff was so evident that one of my first reactions to the ward was, "This is like a prison!" When I found that a staff member had to accompany me on the short walk down the corridor to the laboratory, when I saw patients with "hospital privileges" asking the charge nurse for a pass to go to the gift shop, when I realized that I was forbidden to go out the doors of the ward without permission, I was reminded of the pervasive system of control that I had observed in a maximum security military prison while training there as a reserve officer. For me, as it had been for our prisoners, "being out of place" was an offense against the norms of the total institution. This bit of sociological jargon, "total institution," took on a real and personal significance for me.

Obviously, my initial reaction to the manifestations of the power of the staff over the lives of the patients was negative. It continued so for a couple of days, although I soon learned to accept this power gracefully. On my first morning on the ward, Sunday, I overheard a conversation between another patient and a nurse as to whether my longhaired ping-pong opponent would be allowed to go to the chapel. Apparently his request to leave the ward for this purpose had been approved previously, but now he could not get a pass. When the other patient pressed the nurse for the reason, she replied "He knows why he can't go." My instant reaction was, "My God, are we dealt with like naughty children?" I carefully read the rules of the ward, posted on the wall and discussed in a handbook for patients. Insecure, somewhat lost in this strange milieu, I reacted like a child. If I were the least bit uncertain as to whether it was all right for me to do something, I would go to the nurses' station and ask for permission or approval from one of the young women there, as if she were my mother. I think I was beginning to relive the "good little boy" pattern that had characterized most of my childhood, when I lived in dread of my mother's disapproval.

My surrender to this new source of authority was well illustrated on Monday, when I received a mild but firm reproof for smoking my pipe so much. I did smoke it too much; at home, it annoyed my wife terribly. But when I was depressed and insensitive to everything else, my pipe was very important to me. The resistance of the bit to my clenched teeth and the bite of the smoke on my tongue seemed to be my only sharp contact with the world around me. So, as soon as I finished breakfast, my pipe went into my mouth and stayed there until it was almost time for OT—occupational therapy. Just before my first visit to the workshop, the nurse approached me and said rather sharply, "Lewis, you can't smoke your pipe in OT. You'll have to put it down. I'm tired of your smoking it so much anyway!" Obediently, and feeling almost ashamed, I hastened into my room to empty the pipe into an ashtray and to leave it there. From then on I tried to cut down on the amount of time I smoked it, something my wife had tried in vain to get me to do.

That "staff power" was a recurrent issue in a community in which patients had some kind of citizenship became evident in the first "morning meeting" of patients and staff which I attended. I had found Sunday, the day before, incredibly dull, broken only by a brief walk outside the hospital. In morning meeting it developed that some activities which had been planned in "Patient Government" on the previous weekend had fallen through because of a shortage of staff. Some patients who had taken part in the planning expressed their displeasure with considerable emotion. The discussion soon generalized to the question of just how much the vote of the patients meant in any matter, since the staff could veto any decision at each level of review, all the way up through Doctor B. This sort of discussion was my cup of tea! I jumped into the discussion with vigor, talking like the sociologist I am, analyzing the situation and pointing out analogies to other systems of authority. Still ignorant of what had really been involved, I brought up the issue of denial of a patient's request to go to chapel, dramatizing it as verging on an unconstitutional denial of his rights. Nothing was settled in the discussion, but a lot of feelings were ventilated, with the staff sitting patient and calmly, seeming almost to encourage the attacks on them. At this point I didn't understand what was going on; I didn't know that this was "the name of the game" in the therapeutic community.

During the next few days I gradually learned several things. One was that I would have to play the role of the patient; identification with the staff not only was not permitted but was, I came to realize, not best for me. I could not be my own therapist. This was brought home to me by the remark I evoked from more than one staff member, "Lewis, you're intellectualizing too much!" What did they mean? I didn't understand at first. After all, I am an intellectual— "Intellectualizing" is my trade. An entrenched behavior pattern of mine was standing off and looking at myself and my problems as if I were another person. I had always felt that in this way I developed excellent insight into my problems. The trouble was that when I was depressed, I analyzed my situation as a dilemma about which I could do nothing. When I felt good, I could change, but I was not motivated to do so. In either case, I ended up with what I thought was a brilliant diagnosis but without the slightest sort of action. The only feeling I would express was despair.

Apparently what the staff perceived was that this sort of rational, detached self-analysis led not only to no action but to an inadequate diagnosis. By pushing aside my feelings instead of letting them pour out, I concealed, even from myself, some of the most important things that really "bugged" me—such as an unarticulated belief that some of the demands my wife made on me were really unreasonable. I had always convinced myself that my problems derived entirely from demands stemming from outside the family, from my work and civic involvements. I had persistently denied that there might be the slightest thing wrong with interpersonal relations within my happy family. Now the staff kept pushing me to feel instead of just thinking; they sensed that the fundamental problems that caused my periodic depressions would be exposed only if I allowed my anger, my sadness, my disappointment, to pour out uninhibited by logic, theory, or the need to preserve the image of myself as a "nice guy." In one-to-one impromptu counseling sessions with various staff members I was forced to express myself in this unaccustomed, discomforting manner. Soon I found myself behaving in the same way toward other patients, expressing my displeasure when I did not like the way they acted. I began to interact with other people in this small, intense community with an honesty that I found refreshing.

In this interaction I learned that even though the patients might not have real power, there was great value in our discussing issues as if we were indeed responsible persons. "Feedback" was the label facilely attached to our discussions, but the term is too trite and inadequate to fully characterize what went on. There was feedback, of course, when we were called on to discuss and vote on each other's requests for hospital privileges, ground privileges, or LOA. I was amazed at how quickly I and other patients learned to say things to each other that might be interpreted as adverse to the recipient's petition. All adrift in the same lifeboat, at least some of us seemed to recognize that kindly deceptions were not really helpful. Each of us needed to know what kind of impression he was making on the people with whom he spent most of his waking hours. Our discussions extended far beyond such amateur clinical observations, however. They ranged from seemingly minor matters, such as the problems of housekeeping within the ward, for which we were responsible, to major issues that could become the basis of intragroup hostility.

One major matter was the request of a hallucinating patient that we not have the television on for a period of two days because it made her nervous. Some of her hallucinations included the very disturbing conviction that President Nixon exercised direct, personal control over her life and that television was one of his instruments of control.

149

Her request was discussed with a maturity and a gentleness that I would find rare "on the outside"—in a meeting of my departmental faculty, for example. Her personal desire was not dismissed as simply selfish or crazy; her very genuine concern was treated with respect. Yet the contrary interests of the other patients were clearly and firmly stated. The request was denied, but this was not the end of it. I still have a warm feeling when I remember how our behavior changed after this discussion. No longer was the volume of the TV turned up so high that a patient sitting at the far end of the room could hear it. If it was that loud, someone would turn it down. Those of us who wanted to watch television began to gather closer to the set, so that the volume could be kept low. Moreover, at least for the remainder of that week the television was turned on very infrequently, and then only when someone was definitely paying attention to it. The balance that was achieved between a cherished right and consideration for another person's idiosyncrasy was a model for civilized living.

On another occasion, I found myself at the center of a small storm. At Patient Government on Wednesday night, when weekend activities were planned, the majority of patients from both floors of the ward had voted for ice-skating as the activity for Friday night. On Friday morning, a patient from the other floor polled each of us individually as to whether we would like to change our plans and go to a musical comedy being given at a nearby school. I had seen the play before and did not particularly wish to see it again; furthermore, I had managed to develop a modicum of enthusiasm for ice-skating and had gotten my wife to bring me my skates. Nevertheless, I voted for the play because I got a clear signal that most of the patients on the other floor would prefer this activity. I was following my accustomed pattern of being the "nice guy," who suppressed his own feelings and did what he thought he should, to avoid guilt feelings. I guess I let some of my real feelings slip out, however, and one or two other patients from our floor expressed some disappointment also. A member of the staff assembled us in an impromptu meeting to discuss the decision. Since there seemed to be some dissatisfaction about the poll and its results, each floor was meeting to vote again. First, though, we had to examine why there seemed to be so much feeling about the situation. I didn't know that there was any strong feeling about it, but suddenly I found myself being identified as one of those who was upset by it! Reverting to my analytical, supposedly objective self, I launched into a sociological analysis of how the poll had not seemed impartial to me, since the young lady who asked for my vote made it quite clear that she hoped I would vote for the play. Then I hastened to add that I felt a little disappointed but really didn't care enough to vote against what the majority seemed to want. What was wrong with this, I asked? Plenty seemed to be wrong; I almost felt myself under attack by the two or three staff members in the meeting. Why didn't I feel that I could vote my own preference? It was obvious, I was told, that I did have some strong feelings. Was it constructive for me to try to pretend that I didn't? Would this contribute to harmony in the community? After getting involved in a heated argument, I finally "surrendered"—that's the way I felt about it—and voted against going to the play. Admittedly, part of my motivation stemmed from the fact that an LOA for Saturday and Sunday had been approved for me. I was afraid that if I persisted in voting for the play I might be considered so disturbed that I wouldn't get my pass to go home. Later I realized that this was a groundless fear; indeed, I have to admit that the meeting was not designated as group therapy aimed at me. This turned out to be its effect, however. As I thought about it, I realized that I had been giving contradictory signals, which could take some of the pleasure out of going to the play for other people. When I finally voted "No" to the play, it was the first time perhaps in years that I had asserted a personal preference in a situation of this sort without equivocation, apology, or feelings of guilt. Time and time again I had given my wife just such a begrudging, insincere "Yes" vote when she proposed an activity for us, and she had always seen through me. This had been a constant source of irritation, rendering me a poor companion in what we did and making her feel that she was "dragging me along." While I didn't get my way—we went to the play—the therapeutic community had called my hand and forced me to be honest with them. The lesson stuck with me after my discharge, and I am still practicing at this sort of honesty. Strangely, I now find it easier to say either "Yes" or "No" since I am being honest instead of just nice.

The flow of communication between patients and between them and the staff seemed to me to have a variety of valuable consequences for individual patients. One patient's articulation of the belief that he was really improving, along with quite clear evidence manifest in his behavior, could be a source of hope and encouragement to another— especially if the evidence of improvement came at a time when the second patient was somewhat discouraged. Finally, I am sure that mild, and sometimes not so mild, reproof from other patients concerning antisocial or "crazy" behavior had even greater impact on the subject than did the observations of staff members.

My conception of the power of the staff changed as I reacted to their behavior. I came to feel that is was pervasive and encompassing but essentially supportive rather than threatening. It was the nurses and nurse's aides who exerted this influence, although the therapists actually had greater power over the patients' lives. But a patient saw his therapist only two or three times a week, and then for an hour at a time. On the other hand, at least one member of the nursing staff was on the floor at all times, and usually there were three present. Some of the time they would be busy at the nurses' station, but during most of the day they blended almost unobtrusively into the life of the community. While they were hardly omniscient, very little that a patient did escaped their attention. I soon came to feel that I was, indeed, under constant observation.

The proceedings at the daily afternoon "nurses' report" sustained this impression. At these meetings the morning shift of nurses reported to the afternoon shift on each patient—with the patient sitting there listening as he was "dissected." He was free to offer comments on what the nurses said, as were other patients. What was especially illuminating, however, was hearing a nurse report, in a clinical manner, how you had appeared to feel during the day, what had upset you or pleased you, which of your activities and comments she had found significant—a wide range of behaviors; some might have seemed important to you and others you might even have forgotten.

Against this background, even the smallest supportive gesture from a staff member appeared in a new light; the therapeutic function of the interaction of staff with patients became more evident. If I sat down alone, perhaps in the kitchen with a cup of coffee, a nurse might join me and strike up a conversation as she knitted. It was all very casual, yet I soon realized I was being given an opportunity—and a challenge—to get outside the prison of my mind and share my thoughts and feelings with another human being. On two or three occasions when I was anxious about something—as when my wife was late for visiting hours—it seemed even more evident that the con-versation was not really casual but was a calculated attempt by the staff member to get me over a bad time. On other occasions, it appeared that a nurse saw an opportunity to draw me out about some important area of my life. For example, immediately after one of my wife's visits, a nurse who was closer to me in age than the others steered me into a long discussion of my family life. This impromptu session was almost like psychodrama, with the nurse playing the role of my wife by interpreting how things I said might sound to her.

This almost constant observation and intervention made it very difficult for a patient to withdraw and nurse his troubles in private— something I was certainly inclined to do when I entered the community. If a patient really felt ill, was sleepy, or was acting in a disturbed fashion, he could withdraw to the privacy of his room as long as there was no scheduled activity. Occasionally a patient would, in effect, be sent to his room and temporarily removed from the community by a nurse. It was my impression, however, that if I withdrew on my own initiative, a nurse or nurse's aide would soon be on hand to ask what I was doing and how I felt. I soon reached the conclusion that it was easier to keep active and involved with other people than it was to justify withdrawing into a shell. This change of behavior pattern was, of course, just what I needed to break the cycle of my depression, and it came about without anyone's explicitly prescribing it for me.

I must confess that I became a little paranoid about what I sensed as constant observation of my behavior. There were times, no doubt, when I was more active than I really needed to be. On one occasion I was cautioned by a staff member about becoming too involved in another patient's problems. There was a period when I began to be extremely self-conscious about almost everything I said, wondering, "What will the staff make of this if I say it?" For example, when my doctor completely terminated my medication instead of merely reducing it, as I had anticipated, I remarked facetiously, "He took me off cold turkey!" Immediately I thought, "Oh, Lord, how will that remark be interpreted? Will the staff think that I'm really upset about this when actually I'm happy?" It was not until I really began to feel good and was confident that I was recovering that I felt free to joke, particularly about myself.

Perhaps to some people, subjection to such a system of social control might seem humiliating. To me, it is better described as "humbling," forcing me to come to terms with a simpler, more elementary level of existence than was habitual for me and, at the same time, causing me to revise my priority of values. Things connected with my work, heretofore central in my life, the source of both great pride and severe anxiety, were suddenly banished from my daily schedule and even from my thoughts. The experience was also regenerative; it was as if I were given a chance to go back and relive some parts of my childhood, developing new attitudes in the process.

That this was happening was brought home to me as I was finishing, with pride and satisfaction, my first OT project. I remarked to a therapist, "Hey, I'm the kid whose mother always said he couldn't drive a nail straight. I guess she was wrong!" When I started the project, I had no confidence that I could make anything that wouldn't end up in the trash. I had a similar reaction the night that square-dancing was the patient's activity. As long as I could remember, I had felt self-conscious and inhibited about dancing, and particularly about trying anything new. I had even anticipated ridicule from my wife, herself a free spirit on the dance floor. Now, in the company of my fellow patients, I felt no fear of looking silly or of being laughed at. To be able to let myself go in learning new dance steps was an exhilarating experience.

In the round of life in the hospital it was small things like this, not whether my next book would be a success, that I learned to look forward to. However, to enjoy the simple pleasures that each day might bring, to enjoy merely being alive, had to be learned. When I first entered the ward, I could not imagine how I could survive what promised to be empty, meaningless days in which I would be accomplishing nothing by my usual standards. Within this void, new sources of satisfaction began to take shape. With the four walls of the ward defining the limits of my freedom, an escorted walk to Friendly's or McDonald's became one of the day's highlights. At home in midwinter, I had resisted going out of the house, not appreciating what a privilege this freedom could be. The hospital meals were certainly not gourmet cooking, but each mealtime came to be an adventure. There was the question, "What—if anything—will be good today?" Eating was also one of the relaxed, social activities in which the patients shared. There was usually a lot of joking and much sharing of food. Even the aftermath of each meal, cleaning up the kitchen, was something to do that could give one a sense of accomplishment. Gradually I found myself structuring each day in my mind as I approached it, cherishing what were becoming familiar routines as well as small diversions.

Enjoying life, even finding it tolerable, was not easy at first. During most of the first week I was still depressed and now, in addition, I was lonely. The two very highest points of my day were my morning telephone call to my wife and her visit during evening hours. Yet there was an aura of unreality about these contracts with her: she was in the world outside, and both my mental state and my physical confinement to the hospital made this world seem very far away. For a couple of days I ate my heart out trying to guess when I would be able to get back into that world, a well man again. Slowly I came to realize that this did me no good, that this small area in the hospital was my world for now and that I had to take each day as it came. Yet, as the end of that first week approached, I was determined to get home on LOA. I wasn't sure that I would be able to enjoy a visit home; I was really apprehensive about going; but I would have been desolate had I not been able to go. I protected myself, in a way, by asking that my LOA begin on Saturday morning instead of Friday night, explaining that my wife had to meet our son at the bus station on Friday night.

My visit home was not an unqualified success, although I now believe that it was very beneficial. Life still did not seem as bright to me "on the outside" as I had hoped it would. I still found it difficult to concentrate, and interacting with other people, even my loved ones, was not easy. I knew I was going back to the hospital and I felt somewhat like an outsider in my old, familiar surroundings. I felt that the hospital was really where I belonged. Perhaps in terms of my therapy this was good. It enabled me to commit myself completely to the life of the therapeutic community when I returned. By late Sunday afternoon I realized that while I desperately wanted to feel good enough to prolong my stay at home, I was really ready to go back to my "home" on the ward. It represented a new source of security. More important, it was in the hospital that the work of getting well had to be done and I wanted to get back to work.

Nevertheless, the evening of my return was a low point. No sooner had my family left me than I wanted to be with them again. There was not much to do on the floor that night and the minutes dragged until bedtime. I was glad that I could get a sleeping pill that night to help me escape from my loneliness.

When I awakened the next morning and commenced the week's round of activities, however, things began to change. The daily schedule seemed a familiar, comforting routine. I was eager to get back to my OT project, I looked forward to the discussions that took place in the daily meetings, and I was truly glad to see my friends among both patients and staff. That Monday was the last day during which I had any doubts at all as to whether I was recovering, and rapidly. Two things which seemed very significant happened that night: my medication was stopped, and I had a fabulous time square-dancing. To make the evening perfect, I fell asleep promptly after going to bed although I had taken no medicine since early afternoon.

Whatever the reason, when I got out of bed the next morning my heart was singing. There was no feeling that I would have to force myself to do things during the day—I wanted to be alive and busy. When I had returned from my home visit, I had brought back some work with me, but with little confidence that I would be able to tackle it. Before this day was out I found myself looking for free time when I could get at it. Wonderfully, however, I didn't feel driven to work as I always had before. If someone sat down and wanted to talk, or said "Let's play ping-pong," I could lay aside my task with no feeling of guilt or irritation. The days began to fly by, for now there was always something that I *wanted* to do.

At this time I became aware of a strange but wonderful paradox. During the first week, when I had still had some resistance to being hospitalized and was counting the days until I might be discharged, I didn't feel that I was making sure and steady progress toward that end. After my somewhat disappointing weekend at home, I had come back with a different attitude; I really felt ready to stay as long as I had to. It was just after I had fully accepted the ward as a second home that I really began to feel that I no longer needed it: I was confident that I could go home and function normally any day.

This left me with mixed feelings that came as a great surprise to me. I still wanted to get home but now I saw the ward as a pleasant environment which I would leave with some sadness. Other members of the therapeutic community had become real friends. I felt tremendous gratitude to the staff for the help that I could now see they had given me; I was eager to share with them the joy at feeling alive again. The other patients were friends whom I had come to know better in a short time than I did many friends of long standing on the outside. This was a community in which the members did not hide their problems and their feelings from each other. We all knew that we wouldn't be there unless we had problems. The troubles of my fellow patients had become matters of genuine concern to me; signs of progress were sources of pleasure for me. I was no longer lonely in this community, and I knew I would miss it.

When I went home the next weekend, with the understanding that if all went well I would check out of the hospital on Monday morning, life in my old surroundings proved to have a new luster to it. My recovery was confirmed for me: I could be happy at home but I could also be happy in the hospital. This was a clear signal that it was indeed time for me to be discharged. I could see how the therapeutic community could become a warm, comforting refuge for a person who did not have the strength to manage his own life. When I awakened on my first morning at home after my discharge, I felt a momentary panic at the prospect of having to decide for myself what I would do with the day. I was frightened at the loss of the structured environment of the hospital. This feeling passed quickly as I got up and got busy, but my nostalgia for my hospital friends did not pass away so soon. For a few days I still had the feeling that the hospital was "home" and that I was a visitor to the outside world. My conversation, both with my wife and with my friends, was dominated by references to my experiences on the ward and to my friends there. I was very glad that, just a few days before my discharge, my wife had been able to participate in Family Night, a meeting of patients, their families, and a few staff members. At least she had received a little exposure to the spirit of our community; she had seen me functioning as a patient, not just as her sick husband.

In talking to friends, I found much to my surprise that I was not at all reticent about discussing my illness and my hospitalization. All the fears which had haunted me on the day I entered had vanished. As I watched people interact I would sometimes find myself thinking, "We dealt with our problems better in the therapeutic community than these people deal with theirs. Just who is crazy?"

As I eased back into the business of living in the outside world — loving, playing, working—the homesickness that I experienced at first went away. It must shock my friends, however, when one of them says, "I'm sorry to hear that you have been in the hospital," and I reply, "Thank you—but it was one of the most wonderful experiences of my life!"

1973

37

"Mother-Son Symbiosis"

SARAH E. LORENZ

Three members of the Lorenz family have moved into a psychiatric ward as part of therapy for son Ken, as described earlier in the Admission section. Mrs. Lorenz finds that the mental hospital atmosphere exacerbates rather than resolves family conflicts and leads to intolerable labeling of their behavior.

FOR THE average person, speaking on any subject in a group presents its difficulties. But speaking about the "inner self" before a mixed group of professional and lay people (often including visitors) was like undressing oneself in public. Besides, even if conflict does exist, the individual usually finds it difficult to recognize, let alone discuss. It is usually up to the probing analyst to exhume it. And so I kept my counsel, laying all disappointments to the vagaries of research and reminding myself that we had come here for one purpose and one purpose only: to help Ken.

To this end we could put up with anything. The harassing, puzzling, and frustrating daily meetings. The boredom. Even, yes, even the growing dissension with Cleve [the father], although that situation seemed a dear and terrible price to pay.

My convictions and my emotions vacillated; I was determined to find the good in this place where we had transplanted ourselves at such sacrifice. At the same time I was restless, impatient to get on to the therapeutic phase of the process. If, as the hypothesis saw it, conflict within us played a part in our son's illness, then I wanted to get going in the direction of resolving this conflict. But days passed, weeks, and nothing appeared to progress. Worse, Ken's first burst of

158

responsiveness was short-lived. He was regressing fast. And nobody here would lift a finger to help him!

We were not advised directly to keep hands off. In theory this was a free, self-governed group. But fundamentally the direction was there in many ways, in the meetings, in the unit, whenever a situation arose. Except for two or three nurses who quietly and subtly let me know that they sympathized with my position as a mother, not as some cold bacillus in a test tube, the attitude of everyone seemed to be: ignore him, don't touch him, leave him alone no matter how far he withdraws.

This, even from Cleve!

My husband never does things by halves. Now that Cleve had adjusted to the idea of research he entered into the project with almost the same clinical detachment as those in charge. "We must not deviate from this experiment," he argued. "We must co-operate; it's why we're here."

Experiment . . . yes, he had me there. I thought I had come here for that purpose with open eyes. But when that experiment appeared not to help our son, but only to damage him further, I could not stand idly by. Ken might be their guinea pig, but first he was our son. He had followed us here in innocent trust. And we had brought him, not as an offering on the altar of research, however high and sublime; we had brought him in the blind faith that research might bring a turnabout in his illness and make him whole.

Now that he was apparently to serve only as an object of observation, to lie sick and helpless in his room if need be, I could not bear it. I did everything in my power to draw him out and raged at Cleve for refusing to do likewise. Thus the two people who had entered the project harassed, yes, but united, looking to the future together with hope and love, these two selfsame people became divided, bitterly at odds.

The irony of this was staggering. An aim of the project was the day-to-day observation of emotions and conflicts in parents, to gather clinical data to reinforce the hypothesis. Yet at no point in our lives were our conflicts so deep and unrelenting. By the very fact of our being here we had produced a king-size conflict that should provide data for researchers for a long time to come. Furthermore, here we were, living under glass, with every word and act a matter for analysis. Here we were, uprooted, transplanted, minus the day-to-day contacts of the average family, neighbors, friends, clubs, business

159

associates. Here was a man who in the normal course of events would kiss me good-by in the morning to spend his day in the business world, who instead was now idle and thrown with me hours on end. Here, except for occasional visits, we were minus that other child who completed and enriched the family circle, our younger son.

In addition, we were surrounded at all times by sick people, whose actions were not only bizarre but sometimes frightening. All these things created their own tensions, left their unmistakable imprint. Even had we not differed so acutely on Ken, the very circumstances were far from conducive to a normal relationship. Thus to imagine that any valid observations could be made under such totally abnormal circumstances was not only questionable but absurd. Yet these were the parents who were being viewed microscopically, in the search for clues to other people's abnormal behavior!

Our emotions were a tinder box, our tensions severe, our distress unyielding. When we tried serious discussion it contained more temper than reason. We could no longer communicate; we were becoming, I realized, appalled, like two strangers.

In vain I implored Cleve to join me in an attempt to rouse Ken from his lethargy. As dedicated to his own convictions as I, he refused. We were playing for keeps. If we had chosen to follow the lead of science then we must not falter. At one point Ken reverted to a withdrawn, regressed state that drove me to despair; it seemed that I was swimming against the current to try to help him, and not even my husband held out his hand. Ken refused to budge from his room, refused drink and food for days, with a resulting weight loss of thirty pounds. When no attempt at intervention was made (he had not yet dehydrated, the proposed point of intervention), I was beside myself. Research or no, to me this test-tube approach was just as inhuman as any savagery inflicted on helpless victims of the primitive snakepits.

My thinking became deeply subjective. Living on the unit deteriorated to the point of fighting for emotional survival. Such objectivity as I was able to achieve was on a superficial level. I was first and foremost a mother; it was not within my power to stand by watching the physical and emotional anguish, the deterioration of my own flesh and blood.

Yet in doing what I felt I must to save him, I found myself in a precarious position. With the hands-off policy, including my husband's, circumstances had forced me to provide Ken with his only motivation, the only companionship he received. And so I put "dancey" records on the player and cajoled him into dancing with me. I lured him to the gymnasium, to the movies, or went with him on long walks about the grounds. This activity was alluded to by the nursing staff as a deep dependency, a mother-son symbiosis. This conclusion I felt to be highly chimerical and totally without basis. I felt none of the emotions ascribed to me. It was like being accused of an act one is forced to commit at gunpoint. What they had observed was not the real us, but two people driven together in the desperation of the one's neglect and abandonment. To be so promptly adjudged of anything else tried to temper, my reason, and my soul.

Looking back, reading the simple, naive entries in my diaries, I could not imagine the complications my words and actions would arouse. And looking ahead I could not, luckily, foresee how hopelessly enmeshed I was to become.

c. 1958

III

Release

Introduction

There is a growing tendency in some
quarters to judge the standard of a mental
hospital by the rapidity of patient turnover.
Whilst the quick discharge of patients may
be a praiseworthy feature, it is time we
asked ourselves whether the hospitalization
of the patient was the correct course in the
first instance, or merely the most convenient way of disposing of a difficult
person. . . .

> Dr. T. P. Rees, former superintendent
> Warlingham Park Hospital, England
> *The Patient and the Mental Hospital*

Well, I don't like to think of anyone as
fleeing from us. However, I must say that
there is a large body of persons who do fear
the ministrations of the practitioners of
mental health.

> Dr. Charles Smith quoted in Thomas Szasz,
> *Psychiatric Justice*

Nobody has ever measured, even the poets,
how much a heart can hold. . . . When one
really can't stand anymore, the limits are
transgressed, and one thing has become
another; poetry registers itself on the
hospital charts, and heart-break has to be
taken care of. . . . But heart-break perishes
in public institutions.

> Zelda Fitzgerald, quoted in Nancy Mitford,
> *Zelda*

BLUE JOLTS

The release rate from mental hospitals in the United States is high. Today the average stay is four weeks instead of the six months of twenty-five years ago. This change is part of the broad social movement toward welfare support in the community, including nursing homes and outpatient centers in place of expensive institutionalization.[1] The release process, though, is inconsistent and unfair. Jurist Ronald Rock found that release "is less a matter of medical judgment and more one of welfare expediency,"[2] which means relieving the hospital by finding a person or social agency that will supervise, support, or take legal responsibility for the inmate. The avowedly medical official criteria for release cloak the broad mandate to save hospital expenses. Ironically, mental hospital policy is geared to getting rid of troublesome inmates who by strictly "medical" criteria, are perhaps most ineligible for release. "Passing the Buck" shows staff easing the difficult Wilson boy (see the Admission section) out of the hospital.

Ward personnel sometimes even encourage disruptive inmates to escape. In the case of one of the leaders of a group of unruly teenage inmates, "a member of the ward staff 'inadvertently' helped him to escape" by leaving a door unlocked.[3] "Occasionally an escape is 'planned' by the staff in cases in which the staff wants the patient to show initiative."[4] However, the mass escapes and rebellions portrayed in fiction and film don't take place, though there have been group escapes from institutions for the mentally retarded and "hospitals for the criminally insane."[5] Most inmates have little reason to actually escape from the hospital grounds, since they can "elope" when in town on a pass, or extend their leaves of absence. The United Press selection, "Turning the Tables," is an atypical but amusing account of unwitting staff collusion in an escape. Paradoxically, as nursing instructor Jacquelyn Murray observes in "Threatened with Jail," staff will pressure some inmates to stay and others to leave.

Since most inmates want to "go home"[6] with formal permission, the customary release interview is stressful. (John Martin reports that inmates have died during these interviews.)[7] The inmate must "show insight" by agreeing that he needed hospitalization, and by "making a contrite admission of illness in modestly untechnical terms."[8] He is to thank the doctors for helping him and say that he thinks that he is ready to leave. Judith Kruger describes "The Little Tricks" she used to appear composed and how she obediently promised to seek

166

treatment on the outside. The men in attendant Paul Warr's "Are You Happy Here?" do badly, however—one, because he is too agreeable; the other, because he displays insufficient insight and tact. Similarly, the woman in Robert Perrucci's "She's Obviously Paranoid" seriously hurts her chances by arguing with the doctors. In "Religious Propoganda," Soviet dissenter Shimanov also learns that "to dispute with men whose credit and superior qualifications of mind depend on basically opposite axioms to one's own is a more vain recourse than straw applied to smother a fire."[9] In contrast, doctor-lawyer Donald Johnson cleverly obtains release by fawning cooperation, in "The Head Boy."

Once released, the inmate suffers not only the stigma of "spoiled identity"[10] of "ex-mental patient," but he has for the moment lost a sense of belonging to the family or community from which he has been ejected: "In the hospital, the patient is an enforced member of a group living in an entirely artificial environment bearing no resemblance to anything approaching ordinary home life, but where everything is strange and often frightening.[11] Sociologist Perrucci contends that hospitalization represents "an effort to stabilize the deviant role and reinforce the deviant identity of the victim."[12] The outcast has to resume his disrupted life in the midst of people who accept "the myth of mental illness" (the title of Thomas Szasz's pioneering 1961 book) to the extent of seeing him as imbalanced, immoral, irresponsible, dangerous, and deviate, but certainly not to the extent of showing the kindness they offer the physically ill. Thus, professor of English Anna Mary Wells, having provoked a petulant staff to release her, finds that people on the outside see her as a mental patient, as she illustrates in "Spilled Sugar." In Dr. Glass's account, "Too Sick for this Kind of Work," mental health workers, the very people who profess the most tolerance and understanding of patienthood, reject their former colleagues who have been hospitalized on their own service. In Mrs. Davenport's "Imbalanced," she must struggle to have a physical problem taken seriously. Part II of "The Insanity Bit" shows Seymour Krim's friends shunning him because his hospitalizations stigmatize him as mad. Long institutionalization makes for the most difficult adjustment, as Jack McCabe discovers when he takes his uncle off a chronic ward. (See John Neary's "Institutionalism.")

The former inmate often has trouble finding a good job, particularly in public service and with large corporations, since he must face questions about previous positions and dates of employment, as well as direct questions on "history of mental illness." Depending on the locale, he may be further frustrated by the loss of civil rights such as the vote, and license to drive and marry. If the former inmate tries to make a gradual transition in a halfway house, he will encounter neighbors who protest that "crazy people are roaming the streets." Sans job, home, and expectation of success in the community, he is vulnerable to rehospitalization; indeed, the readmission rate is high. Doctors understandably contrive to protect their hospitalized brethren: "Unfortunately, a psychiatric diagnosis still carries a stigma in many quarters and can be potentially and permanently damaging to a patient's career and future. This is particularly true when the patient is a physician. As a result, we noted a tendency toward assigning a less serious pathologic diagnosis to our colleagues."[13]

The inmate can seek satisfaction in the notion that the whole world is mad. In 1917 Rosa Luxemburg called the world ". . . this huge lunatic asylum in which we live."[14] As she wrote, shell-shocked soldiers in a Budapest hospital were being given strong electric shocks: "The intention was to shock them back to health so they could be returned to the front as quickly as possible."[15] In a world that defines health as combat-readiness, Malcolm Lowry's protagonist on a mental ward in *Lunar Caustic* wonders ". . . what point there was in adjusting poor lunatics to a mischevous world over which merely more subtle lunatics exerted supreme hegemony, where neurotic behavior was the rule, and there was nothing but hypocrisy to answer the flames of evil, which might be the flames of Judgment, which were already scorching nearer and nearer. . . ."[16] But the inmate can take little comfort in imagining the world mad, since doing so credits the possibility that he himself is mad: "In truth, madness is the illusion and those systems to which there seems to be madness are themselves deficient, incomplete; whether they are upheld by doctors, patients, or the subscribing public."[17]

The United States Supreme Court ruled in the celebrated *Donaldson* case in 1975 that a "mentally ill" person cannot be held in a hospital against his will if and only if he is not "dangerous to himself or others"; the institution is not offering treatment; and the inmate is capable of living in the community with the help of friends or relatives (*The New York Times*, August 17, 1975, p. 1).[18, 19] The three criteria are so subject to medical interpretation that the inmate cannot meet them all if the doctors oppose release. Since the court mandated neither a "right to (quality) treatment" (this goal is largely a legal ploy to force release of the great number of inmates who receive little treatment), nor a right to no treatment, foes of involuntary hospitalization want a Supreme Court ruling that involuntary confinement of noncriminals is unconstitutional.[20] Until we no longer harm people by forcing them into mental patienthood, individual human beings, such as the man in Donald Justice's poem, "Counting the Mad," will suffer unconscionably.

38

"Passing the Buck"

LOUISE WILSON

Mrs. Wilson earlier describes admitting her son Tony to a private mental hospital for youngsters (see the Admission section). Three years and $20,000 later, the staff psychiatrists can't agree whether the seventeen-year-old should be sent home or graduated to an adult institution.

The selection ends with the parents' decision to take Tony for "an intensive study to be made in a hospital." The famous doctor who presides over the examination keeps Tony on the locked ward of his mental hospital for six weeks' "observation." He pronounces the boy "paranoid schizophrenic," but even he can't suggest what to do with Tony: "For patients of this sort you simply cannot make plans. If I were in your place I would just take each day as it comes." He relieves the enlightened parents of $3000.

The Wilsons then consult Tony's old psychiatrist, who recommends a colleague who takes youngsters into his home for a fee of $40,000 per year. While they are anxiously floundering about, the family happens to hear of a similar arrangement that costs a mere $10,000 per year. Tony entered this psychiatrist's home and was still there as of 1968, by which time Wilson can frankly express some skepticism concerning the motley of psychiatrists to whom they had subjected Tony:

> They blur together in my mind. Bland men, bland as custard, the face behind the desk with a pad and flying pencil, a quiet manner and nothing to say. You have to admit that, if you want to be truthful with yourself; and lying awake night after night, going over the long years' experience, I have become coldly truthful.
> How many times have Jack and I emerged from one of these conferences—after the cordial thanks and the sincere handshake and "Let's not lose hope, let's keep trying!"—and turned to each

other and remarked, puzzled: "Such a nice man! What did he say?"
And one or the other of us responds: "Come to think of it, what *did*
he say?"

WHEN WE were summoned into our conference they were sitting
around a table: three psychiatrists and two social workers. So this
was it. Here we were at a turning point again. My mind was back
almost three years before to the time of our first visit when we
thought we had found our answer. Now the three years had all but
sped away and here we were again, where we had begun. Musical
chairs.

"We are confronted here, quite frankly," the senior psychiatrist
began, "with a certain difference of opinion. However," turning to
Jack, "that won't astonish you, I'm sure. As a physician, you must
see that happen fairly often in your field too."

Jack smiled politely.

"The question is what should be done with Tony. Doctor Lester
does not share my more hopeful predictions for Tony. I am in favor
of permitting him to try things out at home. He could go to college
as a day student, since it is obvious he could not do well in a
dormitory—"

My heart sank. Home again! What could the man be talking
about? I wanted Tony home, but not like this, not this brooding
pain, this bottled-up rage.

"—and Doctor Lester thinks—well, suppose you express your
opinion, doctor."

We had never met Dr. Lester. He was a saturnine person with a
very direct manner. "I've been seeing Tony for several weeks, very
intensively. I have an entirely different feeling about him. I believe
he is far more highly disturbed than would appear on the surface."

This man was more positive than anyone had been before. Surely
no one would be so positive if he did not have facts upon which to
base his opinion. Jack and I leaned forward intently.

"As a matter of fact, it is my belief that Tony could become
violent at any time, his balance is that precarious."

"Violent, doctor?"

"Yes; when a boy makes the threats that he makes, I believe one

171

has to take them seriously. I am not of the school that holds he may just be letting off steam."

"What sort of threats?" Jack asked quietly.

"Threats to hurt people. Me and other people here if we don't allow him to go home. You, if he does go home and you 'get in his way.'"

"Well, I'm now entirely in the dark," Jack said after a minute. "For years I've been hearing that my son was emotionally disturbed. Depressed. Passive-aggressive. A schizoid personality. But I have never been told that he was capable of violence. Has there been some change, has anything happened to bring you to this opinion?"

"You cannot pinpoint time or place in this field. The damaged psyche doesn't get that way overnight. I would have to do a great deal more work with Tony in deep analysis to ascertain that. I believe this is very deepseated and has been with him a long time."

"I see. What shall we do with him, then?"

I marveled that my husband was able to speak, for I was stunned.

"Well, first of all, I suggest that you give up all thoughts of having the boy come home. Not even for an hour. And secondly, if he were my son, after he leaves here in June I would place him in one of the finest clinics in the country; I can recommend the one where I was fortunate enough to have my training. I believe they will help him there if anyone can."

"And you, doctor?" Jack turned to the senior psychiatrist.

"I disagree with my colleague. Tony is obsessive-compulsive, he is passive-aggressive. But once past adolescence and with continued therapy, of course, you ought to see marked improvement."

"But you have no other solution short of trying things out at home?"

The doctor shook his head. "There is no other place."

I spoke up. "Nobody has asked me, but since I am the one who will have to get along with Tony at home, I want to say that . . . well, I'll need help. I'll need to be told how to do it. I can't even relate to him for an hour when we visit him here. How can I manage with him at home?"

"You will not manage at home as long as your pattern of rejection exists."

"My pattern of rejection?" My heart began to pound.

Dr. Lester opened his mouth to answer me, but he was interrupted gently and firmly by his senior.

"No useful purpose can be served by probing into areas that obviously cannot be changed. Our problem is of the moment."

There was a silence around the table. Then Jack addressed Dr. Lester. "This clinic that you speak of—you say there would be intensive psychoanalysis?

"Yes. The very best."

"But Tony has already had so much."

"Yes, but not in the same way. He hasn't been ready enough for it, old enough. This would be much more intensive." There was a pause. "Unfortunately it is expensive. Twenty-five thousand dollars a year."

"Oh!" I cried.

The doctor turned to me. "You are surprised, I know. You would be surprised to learn that there is a waiting list."

"Then these people are a lot richer than I. I haven't got twenty-five thousand dollars a year, even for my son."

Silence fell again, part depression, part weariness and part embarrassment. Into it came the voice of a social worker, Mrs. Daniels, who had been, I recalled, most intelligent and most helpful when we first had come to The School.

"May I make a suggestion?" she asked. Everyone turned to her.

"Yes, please do."

"Well then, perhaps Tony's parents ought to seek some outside opinions about Tony's future. Suppose we were to supply you with the names of several of the best qualified men in the field of adolescent psychiatry; you could consult with them, perhaps you could find what places are available for short-term treatment in a sanitarium, if that should be necessary, or maybe something entirely different."

Well meant as it was, the suggestion was mere buck-passing. But it was still a good way to terminate the fruitless meeting. So it was decided that The School would compile Tony's records and send them to certain doctors whom we would then go to see.

During the next two months we saw five of them in a long pilgrimage by train, plane and car. Everyone was attached to some clinic or hospital and everyone of course suggested that we bring Tony there for an opinion. All of them, having studied the records, were in agreement that the boy had a personality disorder, but the degree of severity was the moot question. Opinions ranged from the possibility that Tony was indeed capable of violence to the mild view that he was merely going through an exaggeratedly difficult adolescence.

The last man we saw was the aged director of a well-known mental hospital. He was the most prestigious, yet he was the most forthright of them all, the easiest to understand, and the one who seemed to understand us best.

After we had gone through the familiar history, he said to us: "I know that the question which you want to have answered above all others is whether your boy can ever get well. And I have to answer you that I do not know. Exactly as we do not know exactly why he is the way he is, so we do not know whether he will always be the way he is."

Jack sighed. "What would you do if you were in our place?"

"First I would have him graduate from high school. At least he will have a high-school diploma. If there should be a recovery he would then have some tool with which to face the world. Then bring him here and I will work with him in therapy. Perhaps I shall be able to tell you more after that."

He was a gentle man with the tender qualities of the old and seasoned. But for all his gentleness and kind smile, there was no hope in this room either. What if we were to bring Tony here for psychotherapy? He had been having it for so long and we had got nowhere. Would this not be simply more of the same?

We thanked him and rose to go. But he was not quite finished. "There is one more thing I want to say to you. I am sure you have a busy practice and I know you have spent a great deal on your son. But unless you are a very rich man"—he paused, feeling for the words—"well, you can impoverish yourself. I have seen it so often. I have seen parents deprive their other children and deprive themselves until it hurt. And in the end it made no difference anyway. Don't do it, doctor."

We walked down the long drive in the gray November.

"What was he telling us, Jack, about not spending too much? That finally and after all we may have to go to a state hospital?"

"What do you think?" Jack countered bitterly.

So we drove home through the lowering afternoon. Another day, another journey, another flare of hope come to nothing.

I must, I simply must, get over this persistent, naive nourishing of hope, I lashed at myself silently. Here we had until recently been planning for graduation and college; nobody had given us any

174

reason to think otherwise. On the contrary, we had been fed on hope. Now suddenly, matter of factly, almost casually, the word "hospital" was being bandied about. How had all this happened without our realizing it?

"Listen here," Jack spoke with sudden determination. "I'm going to take the bull by the horns. I'm going to make my own arrangements for an intensive study to be made in a hospital. I want a final opinion once and for all. I can't make sense out of anything I've been told because I get two different stories on the same day, and the same man has a different story to tell on different days. I want to know what is the matter with my son and what to do for him."

"How long would such a study take?"

"About a month or six weeks, I should think."

"I don't think Tony will go. I'm sure he won't."

"Then he'll have to be taken. We must know where we stand."

The School was completely in agreement with Jack's proposal. I believe they welcomed it because they themselves had no idea what to do with Tony.

c. 1959

39

"Turning the Tables"

UNITED PRESS

What a clever inmate can escape by hospitalizing a staff psychiatrist casts doubt on the mental hospital assumption that "patients" are radically different from "doctors." The incident is not unique: Sociologist Walter Dees edited an attendant's account in which an inmate disarmed a sheriff and almost committed him with papers drawn for himself—but had forgotten to take the officer's identification.[1] Similarly, psychiatrist Miriam Gould recounts that she was locked overnight in a seclusion room when she responded to a ward call at two in the morning in an inmate-type bathrobe and carrying ward keys that the attendant assumed stolen.[2]

In another instance, a nurse confided to lobotomist Walter Freeman that superintendent Coyne Campbell of the mental hospital at which she worked had experienced "tremendous bouts of intoxication that required hospitalization in his own sanitarium."[3] More recently, during the 1975 filming of a film about mental hospitalization entitled *Hurry Tomorrow,* an innocent act led to a crisis of mistaken identity: "One of the filmmakers, Richard Cohen, tells the story about his cameraman who went into a closet to load some film. An attendant ran up to another and said, 'Someone's in the closet reading the Bible.' They grabbed the cameraman and proceeded to drag him toward the confinement room until the mistake was brought to their attention by another member of the crew. Then they all had a good laugh."[4]

JACKSON, LA., Jan. 1 (UP)—A mental patient who turned the tables on a staff psychiatrist and had him admitted to a hospital as an alcoholic was back in the institution himself today.

176

Dr. L. F. Magruder, superintendent of the East Louisiana Mental Hospital, reported that Oscar Hoffman surrendered to the Depaul Mental Sanitarium in New Orleans and was returned to the hospital here.

"We expect him to stay this time," the superintendent commented.

The escapade began on Christmas Day when Hoffman and a staff psychiatrist, Dr. Edwin C. McGowan, took a "little pleasure drink to celebrate Christmas" at the hospital. After some imbibing, they decided on a "little trip."

During the five-day trip, Hoffman and Dr. McGowan visited Baton Rouge, Jackson and New Orleans, leaving behind "plenty of empty bottles," according to the authorities.

Finally, they ended up at the Hotel Dieu (a hospital) in New Orleans. Hoffman told the attendants he was a psychiatrist and that Dr. McGowan was under his care and he wanted him admitted. Hoffman seemingly played his part well and Dr. McGowan was admitted as an "alcoholic" patient.

Then Hoffman went out to Dr. McGowan's car and, with $320 of the doctor's money, drove off. Hoffman continued his drinking spree with a woman companion, authorities said.

At a bar on the outskirts of the city, Hoffman ran up a $60 bill and pawned Dr. McGowan's car to pay it. And finally, while the authorities searched for Hoffman, he walked into Depaul Sanitarium and identified himself.

1949

40

"Threatened with Jail"

JACQUELYN E. MURRAY

Nursing instructor Murray studied decision-making on three differing wards of a large state mental hospital. Over a period of ten weeks, she attended a total of 104 meetings, variously involving staff, inmates, and relatives. She concludes, "The message must have been plain to the patients that the procedure of voting was part of the game plan but had no meaning as far as decision making was concerned. They really were not to be involved in the decision making."

In the course of her observations, she saw how staff pressures unobliging inmates and relatives to accept the hospital's decisions regarding transfer, release, and nonrelease.

STAFF USED various threats to influence balky patients and relatives to conform with their decision. Most commonly with patients, threats took the form of withholding discharge. Another common practice was to threaten patients with transfers to longer term units or other hospitals if they did not cooperate with the staff's decision. In some cases, restriction of privileges was threatened, and in one extreme case the patient was threatened with jail for failure to comply with a staff person's decision.

Relatives were threatened, also, usually in conjunction with getting them to sign transfer papers or to accept the patient for a home discharge. This type of threat took place in therapists' offices during relative-staff conferences or during phone calls from therapists to relatives. Threats took the form of reports to relatives by staff members that the patient was in danger of being violently abused by

178

other patients on the unit, that they would be involved in some kind of police action if they didn't comply, or that home visiting privileges would be taken away from the patient. Another technique was for therapists to invite the relative to the hospital where he was met by a group of staff members (four or five) who would collectively put pressure on him to comply with their decision.

c. 1973

41

"The Little Tricks"

JUDITH KRUGER

Mrs. Kruger entered a mental hospital when she tried to commit suicide after the birth of her child. Her insightful portrait of her release interview conveys the candidate's tension and the little deceptions she feels obliged to practice to gain release. She was discharged a week later.

SINCE LUNCHTIME they have been chanting at me, singly, or in groups, 'Did'ja pass, did'ja pass, did'ja pass?"

I shrug my shoulders and smile. 'I don't know. I think so. I don't know.'

'How wuzzit, how wuzzit, how wuzzit?' the chorus asks.

I give them a quick nod of the head. 'Pretty good. Not hard.'

'Whadid they askyou, whadid they askyou?' the voices rise.

'Some questions. Not many. A few questions,' I reply. Then I stop the music with 'every case is different,' my palms up and open in apology that I cannot tell them more. I remember Laura. I had thought she was unduly evasive when I pressed her for details after her Staff conference. Now I understand.

They're busy now, sitting out here on the benches and grass. I think they're through with me. Now I can mull the thing over; savor it with private pleasure. . . . It went well. Very well. When the student nurse came for me I looked at my hands. They were still and calm. That was a good sign.

'Am I the only one from Ward A today?' I asked her.

'Yes. There aren't too many hold-overs from the summer. Therapy's started again, you know.'

180

'Yes.' I thought of Bertha in the insulin ward.

'You nervous?'

'No. I feel good. I was more nervous about getting shock treatments. I hated them. I—*(Wrong to say that, You're not safe yet. Don't talk so freely. She's just liable to—)* I mean at first. They helped me. They really did.'

When we stepped off the lift I recognized the Admissions ward immediately. Was it only seven weeks ago that I lay in that big room over there wrapped in terror? I saw the fat old Negro woman lumber past. She was still wearing the same stocking cap on her head. I thought, probably on her way to beg a glass of juice for another new admission.

'Wait here a minute. I have to pick up another one.' She left me in the hall opposite the office where I first saw Doctor Manning. It was empty now. Sunlight was streaming on the desk and chairs. But I could still see him as he looked that night, his legs crossed high, his eyes appraising me as I pleaded for a transfer. And I heard myself crying and begging, struggling for coherence from a mind disorganized with fear and depression. My cheeks flushed hot with shame. But I knew that if ever I had a relapse I would be as helpless to control myself as I had been that night. When you are suffocating, there is no time for reason and decorum. You yell for help.

'O.K., let's go.' The nurse was back with a middle-aged woman walking next to her. 'Letty, this is Judith', she said.

'Hello. How are you, Letty?' I spoke up bright and friendly.

She didn't answer me. She wound a strand of straggling grey hair round her ear and wiped her hands on the front of a dirty cotton dress.

What the hell's the matter with her? She's going to Staff. She's being considered for release. And she won't even say hello. Look at her. So messy and dirty. In my ward we shower and change into our best dresses. We set our hair and put on fresh make-up and spray ourselves with cologne. And this one! Bet she passes, too!

We crossed the ward and took another lift ride and came off into a large waiting-room. I remembered this floor. We passed through here on the way for our spinals. From the adjoining offices the click-clack of typewriters punched the air.

Funny, I thought. Or is it? Only a few months ago I had a desk in an office and banged on my typewriter like that. Now I sit here in a mental hospital, waiting for my release.

181

About half a dozen patients were scattered on the benches. The nurse from my ward and two others stood to one side, holding case-history folders. Directly opposite the benches was a green door on which was lettered the word 'STAFF'.

White-coated technicians passed by. Orderlies wheeled equipment trays on and off the lift. Secretaries minced along on high-heeled polished pumps, their heels clattering on the cement floor.

It's like Grand Central Station. We are sitting in the waiting-room. Waiting for a ticket to freedom. We carry no luggage. Just hope. Our minds and bodies are filled with it, breathing it, screaming with it. We don't talk. But when our eyes meet we smile a tight fleeting smile to acknowledge our mutual journey. Some of us fidget and squirm. Others sit quietly, hands folded in our laps. One of us is biting her nails.

It was I. The waiting made me restless. I wanted to walk round or talk to the nurses, to do something active. The tension was building. I ran my fingers along the slats of the bench. I crossed my legs and then uncrossed them. I smoothed the front of my dress.

Creased already. Hate it when dresses get creased, get dirty. Want them clean. Ready to wear but not to wear. Afraid to touch. Oh, God. Felt like this two months ago. Now it's come back. Why now? I'm better. I know I'm better. Just getting a little nervous, that's all.

I went over to my nurse. 'Excuse me, I was just wondering. They take us in turn, don't they? I mean, those other women, they're all ahead of me?"

'Yes. Impatient?

'A little.'

'Once they start, it goes pretty fast. There! They've opened the door. Now go and sit down. It won't be long.'

When a nurse came out of the Staff room we sat up straight and tall, as grade-school children do when the teacher comes into the room. She didn't look at us. She took the folders from the student nurses, walked back to the Staff door, opened the first folder, and called out, 'Djendjielewski!'

A tiny blonde woman popped from her seat like a jack-in-the box. What a name, I laughed inside. She'll be out in a minute. They'll ask her just one question: Spell and pronounce your name. If she does that, she's ready for anything.

I'm silly. I'm making fun of things. Playing with absurdities. Looking for relief in ridicule. Relax. Look out of the window. Count the flowers on your dress. And the tiles on the wall. Get your mind away from that Staff door.

The door opened and the little blonde came out. The nurse called another name. The student nurse was right. It doesn't take long. Then another name, and another. Then—

'Kruger.'

'Here!' I moved to the door. My heart was pounding.

Weren't going to be frightened, were you? Would be a cinch, remember? And now you're hot and cold. There's a hole where your stomach should be and your tongue is thick and dry and burning.

'Over here, Judith. On that chair.' I had been staring at the green rug under my feet until I eased into the chair. Then I looked up. The room was filled with doctors. They were sitting two and three deep behind a long mahogany table.

Is this the Staff? It looks like a medical convention!

'Good morning Judith.'

Who's talking? So many I can't tell.

'Good morning.' I spoke to the far end of the table, my eyes trying to locate the voice.

'How are you feeling?"

Well. Pretty well.'

Got the adverb right, didn't you? Now if I could just see who— There she is. Big grey-haired woman. Hair piled on her head. Big brooch on her dress. Nice face. Motherly. Looks like someone I knew.

'Do you think you're ready to go home?'

Doctor Manning. There on the left. No smile. No sign. Nothing to show he's my doctor.

'Yes. I think so.'

Easy now. Your hands. Relax them. And look at him. Your head a little to one side, your face composed in polite attention. The little tricks. Remember?

'Are you still afraid of the baby?' He asked.

'No. I've come to accept him. I'm more at ease. I enjoy taking care of him now. When I've gone home it felt good to see him and hold him.'

O.K. Cut it. The more you say, the more chance for a blunder.

'Who's taking care of your baby?'

The woman again. Now I know. My art teacher in Junior High. The spit'n' image.

'My mother. She's living with me.'

'And she'll stay on?"

'Oh, yes. As long as I need her.'

'You went to college, didn't you?'

'Yes.'

'What was your major?'

'Home Economics.'

'Well,' she plumped in the chair and smiled, 'I don't think you'll have too much trouble with the house and baby care.'

Silly. She means well, but so silly. Doesn't know how little I was suited for Home Economics. Don't answer. Just smile. Wait for the others to talk. I see Doctor Heineman. He ought to be good for a question or two. Well? Why are they staring? I'm not a freak, am I? Watch it now. Hold that half-smile, that sweet expression. Don't get rattled.

'I understand you'll start therapy as soon as you're home?' The woman again.

'Yes. Right away. I already have a doctor.'

'Well, I think that will be all for now. Unless there are any more questions?' She turned to the others. There was no response. 'We'll notify your husband. Good luck to you, Judith.'

'Thank you. Thank you very much.'

Get up slowly. Don't push the chair. There's the nurse coming for you. She was waiting by the door all the time. Follow her out. Don't look back. You'll have to say thank you again. Few steps more. Door open now. Door closed. Now breathe. Deep. It's over. It's all over.

c. 1957

42

"Are You Happy Here?"

PAUL WARR

Attendant Warr observes two release interviews, including one of a harmless man who would have had a reasonable chance to adjust on the outside.

ON THE morning of this powerful gathering it fell to the student nurse and any willing patients he could find to give the room a thorough polishing. Windows were cleaned and a smoky little fire set going in the black-leaded grate. A table was set out with chairs, their backs against the window. This ensured that the light would fall on the patient's face, leaving the telltale expressions of the psychiatrists in deceptive shadow. Such matters are very important, especially when one is dealing with highly strung and often strong people. The table was covered with green felt. The case papers of people to be interviewed were brought by student nurses from other wards. They spent the waiting time leaning on the table, scanning the pages, hunting through these incredible chronicles of humanity run off the rails. Looking through some of the long entries which detailed progress and retrogression, advance and setback, it was quite astonishing to realise that any of these people had ever managed to reach a stage where they were considered fit for a psychiatric board and, perchance, freedom.

The board itself, looking like a brains trust about to take part in a broadcast, met at eleven and agreed the number of patients to be dealt with before lunch at one o'clock. A breakdown of the time schedule showed that most sessions allowed a patient about twenty minutes in which to answer the questions put by various psychiatrists, justify

185

himself in the eyes of the board as a whole and then add any details about his mental processes he felt to be vitally important to the issue at stake. Three-quarters of an hour would not have been too long for many of the more complex patients. The tight time-table had an infectious tenseness which communicated itself to patients sitting outside, awaiting their turn.

Patients were escorted to the board from other wards by student or staff nurses, depending upon who was free to shoulder the responsibility. In actual fact, there was little responsibility attached to it and the majority of escorts passed the time of day in the ward clinic, drinking tea, or popping over to the nurses' home for a chat with their girl friends who happened to be off duty. The queue of waiting patients sat on hard chairs in the day room. Some attempted to chat among themselves about 'normal' topics, but the atmosphere was tight with expectancy. Each knew that his turn was coming, that he would be required to talk about very personal and private matters to a group of people, only one of whom he knew at all well. This would be the psychiatrist he had seen regularly during his stay. He hoped, as a waiting man once confided to me, that the psychiatrist would help him 'if I get stuck.' I assured him that he would receive every consideration, but I had just come out of the room after waiting while a patient was examined and I could not hold out much hope. The word 'travesty' kept running through my mind, and it would not be suppressed.

It was seldom that a student nurse was able to remain during the examination of patients, but on this occasion I took a man inside and for some reason stayed on, standing behind the examiners. It was a warm, sunny day and several flies buzzed about on the window-pane. I swatted two or three of them and my little massacre was noticed by a junior psychiatrist. He left his chair behind the table and came to watch me. At last he, too, felt impelled to kill. 'Odd little things, flies,' he whispered. I nodded. In the background the questioning was going on. As soon as my companion in the killing game went back to his seat, I perched on a stool in the corner. Unnoticed, I took out a notebook and made a shorthand note of what was happening. This is a transcription:

Q.: You applied for this board, didn't you, John?

Patient: I did apply for it. I thought I might—

Q.: Good. I'm glad you applied for it. It shows initiative when patients do things like that.

Patient: I'm glad you're glad.

(Pause. Cigarettes being lit, mumble of conversation between the members of the board.)

Q.: Now, I see from your case history that you came here after three unsuccessful suicide attempts.

Patient: That's right. I was fed up at the time.

Q.: Wasn't that a silly thing to do? Couldn't you control yourself?

Patient: I felt desperate. I—I want to go now.

Q.: Go from this hospital, you mean?

Patient: I want to go home.

Q.: So that you can try and kill yourself again?

Patient: That's not true! I wouldn't try again. I was silly, I know, and I wouldn't do it again now. I feel a lot better, sir. You can see I am a lot better, can't you?

Q.: How does your wife feel about all this; how does she feel about having you at home again?

Patient: I don't know.

Q.: Haven't you asked her whether she wants you at home? That is very important to us all. Somebody will have to be responsible for you when you go home, John.

Patient: I don't want anybody to be responsible for me. I want to be responsible for myself. That's why—why—I—why I tried to kill myself. I wanted to teach them all a lesson. They fussed me about and I wanted to live by myself.

(One psychiatrist to another in a whisper audible to me: 'He shows asocial traits. . . .')

Q.: I see.

Patient: I could get a room in London somewhere and live by myself and I'd make an allowance to my wife. Would that do?

Q.: Don't you remember that you have some children? There's your son and your two daughters. How will they manage if you go on like this? They are still at school.

Patient: I'll try. I'll try very hard for them. I'll try hard for you, too.

Q.: It's for them you should try, John. It's nothing to do with us, you know.

Patient: You will let me go out of this place, won't you? I want to go home.

Q.: We shall have to think about that. You will be told in due course, John. You may go back to your ward now. You will be told.

John left the room. As soon as the door had closed, the chairman

187

opened the case papers and made a mark on the relevant sheet of paper. 'He's quite unsuitable, of course. Give him another three months and we'd better see him again.'

There was one patient in whom I had a long-standing interest. He was a middle-aged man who, until his mind let him down, held the secretaryship of a learned society, a post paying about £750 a year. He was a bachelor and lived simply, enjoying his work, though he was not very interested in the society itself. Most of his spare time was whiled away attending free lectures at various art galleries and museums. Once in a while he went to the cinema and about three times a year to the theatre, though this was reserved for one month of the year for which he saved a definite sum of money. He was systematic in his habits and had no interest in the opposite sex. In his youth—this was revealed during an abreaction—he had an affair with a girl who turned out to be faithless. Her wanton attitude broke his heart and he renounced for ever his interest in women. For a time he made a friend of a young man, who one day admitted that he was homosexual and found it hard to control himself. This horrified the older man, and again he began to view human society with a jaundiced eye, retreating into a tough shell of his own making. For a time he dabbled with the idea of taking up sketching, but this proved too difficult. When he took pad and pencils into the streets, he created too much attention. He gave it up in favour of writing, and in due course sold one or two simple stories to magazines. Then he met a professional writer, who told him to write for women's magazines if he wanted to make real money. This he did, and, after a long apprenticeship of studying exactly what the magazines wanted, sold a romantic tale to a national magazine. It was published in due course and, coincidentally, a member of the society for which he worked noticed the byline. Unlike many who write for women's magazines, he had not bothered to adopt a pseudonym. The staggering (to the society) discovery caused a mixture of amusement and disapproval. He felt uncomfortable when he had to attend meetings. Then he began to wonder whether they were laughing at him behind his back. At the earliest opportunity he fled to his furnished room, locked the door and threw himself on the bed, unable to marshal his thoughts. Next morning he wrote to the chairman, tendering his resignation.

For several weeks he lived on his savings, but they dwindled at such a rate that he was eventually evicted from his room for non-payment of rent. A policeman found him wandering on the Embankment.

Because he was unable to answer for himself, he was taken into custody and appeared before a magistrate, who immediately remanded him for a medical report. The authorities recommended that he be placed in a mental hospital for observation. It took many weeks of trying to gain his confidence, several abreactions and dozens of interviews with the psychiatrists before his story was pieced together. There is nothing very sensational in it, merely the sombre tale of a man's inability to cope with life.

I spent a lot of time with this patient. Gradually but steadily he told me about himself, but only when I said that I, too, used to feel afraid of what people would say and how they would react. I told him that I had to some extent managed to brutalise my outlook so that the greater part of my susceptibilities were intentionally blunted and I no longer gave a damn for people who presumed to judge me. 'It's what I think of myself that matters,' I insisted, recalling the words of an old bookseller who said the same thing to me when I was a boy.

It became obvious that the patient was encouraged to show improvement. He quickly integrated himself into life in the ward and was later put in charge of other patients, most of whom were inferior in mentality. He polished floors, helped with the washing up and was able to go to the canteen on shopping errands for people. He took an administrative hand and in the evenings was allowed access to the drug cupboard. He took out all the relevant bottles and put them on the trolley, carefully polishing the medicine glasses and lining up the pill-boxes until the duty nurse was ready to dole out the doses.

When he reached this peak of hospital perfection without once blotting his copybook, the charge nurse mentioned it to the psychiatrist, who undertook to make arrangements for his appearance at a board. The patient was not told what was happening. We saw to it that he took on more responsibility. As the date of the board drew nearer it seemed quite sure that he would soon be released to take up a normal life outside in the world he had once shunned.

On the day of the board he was told that he would be interviewed by several psychiatrists in a couple of hours. He seemed quite happy about it and asked me several questions. I told him that if he could overcome any fear he might be feeling he stood a good chance of leaving the hospital for ever. He nodded and smiled. 'It would be very nice to go away from this place. I've been happy here, but it isn't— well, it isn't really a normal life, is it, nurse?'

By the time I took him to the board he was well primed to deal with

189

any awkward questions. I helped him by posing hypothetical queries while we waited. He answered them naturally and, I thought, sensibly.

As we entered the room the psychiatrists stopped talking and the chairman said: 'Sit down there where we can see you.' He glanced at his watch. It was quarter to one, a fact I had not noticed until that moment. Promptly at one they always adjourned for lunch. It was impossible to do anything about it now. I knew that they had endured a heavy morning with many awkward patients to deal with.

'Now—er—there's one thing I want to ask you.' The chairman fiddled with his spectacles.

The patient said: 'Yes, sir?'

'I want to know whether you are happy here.'

Without any hesitation the patient replied: 'Oh yes, I'm quite happy here.'

The chairman glanced at his colleagues. 'I don't think there is anything else, is there?' Then to the patient: 'Would you mind waiting outside?' To me he said: 'Nurse, you can take his case papers. I'll initial them for you.'

The patient was in the corridor, out of earshot. The chairman opened the file. After scratching his initials on the appropriate page, he slammed it shut. To his colleagues he said: 'I've always maintained that if a patient is happy in a place like this, he *must* be mad!' There were appreciative titters as he handed the file to me. It dawned on me that the patient was not going to be discharged after all. He had been condemned to another three months in the hospital on the strength of the answer to a single question: *Are you happy here?*

I did not have the heart to break the news to the man, but left it to the charge nurse. After that, the patient seemed to lose all trust in the nurses. He reverted to introversion and refused to help in the ward. For all I know he is still there, sitting in a day room, thinking his puzzled disordered thoughts, which, for a brief span, threaded themselves together to lift him half-way to freedom.

c. 1954

43

"She's Obviously Paranoid"

ROBERT PERRUCCI

Sociologist Perrucci suggests that release panels try to elicit "pathological" responses from the inmate seeking release so they needn't focus on the subject's possibly unclear home situation or legal status. They anxiously extend and broaden their questioning in an effort to draw out inappropriate answers. When they succeeded, Perrucci observed ". . . a sort of 'tension release' effect whereby anxieties of staff members become redirected toward the patient in a highly emotionalized manner."

In support of his contentions, Professor Perrucci transcribes a release interview he witnessed at a 2400-inmate state mental hospital. In spite of the candidate's having had lobotomy and shock, and the fact that she comes from a "schizophrenic ward," she is wholly rational during her interview. Her honest and realistic statements lead the staff to label her paranoid.

DR. HAND: The next on is ____, a discharge request. She says she can get a lab job in Benton Hospital. Would you tell us something about her, Mrs. Rand [*the patient's ward nurse*]?

Mrs. Rand: Well, ____ has been after a discharge for a while now. I asked Dr. Powell if we shouldn't try, and he said maybe we should. I think it's a shame to keep her here. She's a very bright girl, and she's really learned her lab work. Lately, she has refused to take her medicine. She says it doesn't help her; and besides, she says she doesn't need us to take her medicine.

Dr. Hand: I have a note here from her work supervisor indicating that she works well in the lab and has picked up a great deal.

Dr. Miller: Shouldn't we wait for Dr. Powell before we handle her case?

Dr. Hand: No, he won't be able to make it today, so we'll have to go on without him. Will you show her in, Dr. Craig?

(*Patient enters.*)

Dr. Hand:

Q. I see where you want to get a job at Benson Hospital.

A. Yes, I talked with their lab director last time I was in Benton and he was interested.

Q. Do you think you would like lab work as a permanent job?

A. Oh, yes, I enjoy my work here very much.

Q. It's really not easy work running all those tests. Are you bothered by the blood tests?

A. No, I don't mind them.

Q. Do you know who the governor of ＿＿ is?

A. [*Appropriately answered*].

Q. Do you remember when you first came to Riverview?

A. [*Appropriately answered*].

Dr. Craig:

Q. How do you know you'll get a job at Benton if you're discharged?

A. I told you I talked to the lab director, and he was interested.

Q. Suppose he's not as interested as he appeared to you? Where will you work if you can't get in at Benton Hospital?

A. I think I know my lab work well enough to get a lab technician job somewhere.

Q. Well, let's see how much lab work you really know.

(Dr. Craig *asks the* patient *more questions pertaining to various procedures and lab tests. After the response,* Dr. Craig *indicates that the patient does know her lab work.*)

Dr. Hand:

Q. How do you get along with the other patients?

A. Not very well. I have a few close friends, but I don't socialize with the other patients.

Q. What bothers you about the other patients?

A. Oh, I don't know. I just don't like living in the hospital.

Q. Do you think we've helped you while you've been here?

A. No, I don't.

Q. What kind of treatment have you had here?

A. Lobotomy and shock.

Q. Do you think it's helped you or tortured you?

A. I think it's tortured me.

(This response brings a stir from others present at staff.)

Q. You mean that we did these things just to torture you?

A. Oh, no, I'm sure that when they give shock they mean to help. I don't think they have.

Dr. Stone:

Q. Besides not liking it here, why do you want to go to work?

A. For one thing, I want to start earning my own money, and making my own way.

Q. If you want to make money, we can probably find plenty of opportunities for you to make money right here.

A. You mean like washing cars. I'm already doing that.

Q. [in an annoyed tone] No, I don't mean washing cars. You could probably work full-time in the lab right here on a work placement.

A. I already asked Dr. Galt about an opening in histology, and he said there wasn't any. Anyway, I'd do much better if the hospital would free me.

Dr. Hand:

Q. What do you mean, "free you"?

A. Well, it would be just like the other work placements I've had. You're never really free.

(It was at that point in the staffing session that the observer noted the beginnings of the change in staff behavior. The patient's response about "never really being free," was followed by the exchange of glances among the physicians. These glances indicated that they had, so to speak, "picked up the scent." Staff participation at this point no longer followed the orderly procedure of the staff director asking individual members if they had any questions. The physicians spoke whenever they wished, sometimes cutting in on each other, and sometimes several speaking at the same time. The normal speaking tone vanished as pronouncements and accusations were directed at the patient.)

Q. But if you stayed here on a work placement you'd be free to come and go on your own time. It would be just like a job.

A. No. You would still be controlling me if I stayed here.

Dr. Craig: [cutting in]

Q. Do you mean we control your mind here?

A. You may not control my mind, but I really don't have a mind of my own.

Q. How about if we gave you a work placement in _____; would you be free then? That's far away from here.

A. Any place I went it would be the same set-up as it is here. You're never really free; you're still a patient, and everyone you work with knows it. It's tough to get away from the hospital's control.

Dr. Stone [*cutting in*]: That's the most paranoid statement I ever heard.

Mrs. Rand: How can you say that, [*patient's first name*]? That doesn't make any sense. [*nurse is standing at this point*] It's just plain crazy to say we can control your mind.

(Nurse Rand *turns to* Dr. Stone *who is looking at her.*)

Mrs. Rand: [*still standing*] I had no idea she was that sick. She sure had me fooled. [*turning to* PATIENT *again*] You're just not well enough for a discharge, [*first name*], and you had better realize that.

Dr. Stone: She's obviously paranoid.

(Immediately following Dr. Stone's remark, Dr. Craig stood up, followed by social worker Holmes. Dr. Stone himself then stood up to join the others, including Nurse Rand, who had been standing for some time. It should be noted that this took place without any indication from Dr. Hand, the staff director, that the interview was completed. He then turned to the patient and dismissed her. After the patient left, the standing staff members engaged themselves in highly animated discussion. Nurse Rand was involved in making general apologies for having indicated support of the patient's discharge request at the beginning of the staff meeting. Drs. Stone and Craig were engaged in monologues interpreting and reinterpreting the patient's statements. Amid the confusion, Dr. Hand managed to comment, "I guess there's no need to vote on her; it's quite clear.")*

After leaving staff, the observer returned to the ward to speak with the patient in question. She was very disappointed and bitter. Among her remarks was her accusation that Dr. Powell had never really wanted her to get a discharge, for if he did, he would have been at staff to support her request. However, the patient did appear to show some insight into what had taken place at staff. She made the following remark: "I did learn something from that staff, though. If I ever get a chance to go again, I'll keep my big mouth shut, and I'll lie like hell. This time I said what I really felt, and look what happened."

---

*Although it may appear that the picture of confusion presented here is quite overdrawn, the observer could not help but respond to the very marked aspects of this staff meeting as compared to any other staff meeting he attended. If the descriptive account takes on the aspects of a caricature, it is primarily because of the observed departures from the expected.

c. 1967

44

"Religious Propaganda"

GENNADY M. SHIMANOV

Because he was giving religious instruction and holding family prayers along with his wife, Alla, in their home, Shimanov was removed from his job as a Moscow factory watchman and taken to Kashchenko mental hospital. Two years earlier he had lost his job as a detachment commander in the Internal Guard Corps after the secret police (KGB) summoned him for questioning about his acquaintance with dissidents Vladimir Bukovsky and Aleksei Dobrovolsky. The fact that Shimanov has been in Gannushkin mental hospital seven years earlier, for reasons he does not specify, does him no good either once he arrives at Kashchenko hospital.

His psychiatrist, section head Herman Leonidovich, explains to Shimanov, "You see, what you do is called religious propaganda. Of course, we have freedom of conscience and freedom to conduct religious services . . . but freedom to make propaganda for religion is something we have not got. Such activity is stopped by law." Shimanov objects, "Everything I do, Herman Leonidovich, is completely within the law. The fact is that the words 'religious propaganda' can be understood in different ways. It is possible to interpret the mere presence of faith in someone as propaganda; wearing a cross, also." The doctor counters, "I agree. Perhaps you have not been going outside the framework of the law. But what significance does that have? In actual fact you do harm to the existing regime, all the same, by bringing back straying sheep to the Church. And you know yourself, Gena, that this regime is pretty strict . . . and will not put up with such activity."

Herman Leonidovich claims to be acting in his patient's interest. He advises Shimanov, "But why, having weighed up everything carefully, should you not choose a way in which you can keep your life, your freedom, and the welfare of your family? After all you only have to give up what is really not essential, what may destroy you

195

without doing anyone else any good . . . just bear in mind that the forces are too unequal, that in this situation any struggle means suicide . . . And what has religion to say about suicide? It disapproves . . . You see . . . But it's your affair. I don't want to influence your decision. If you want to destroy your life, and with a clear conscience, I've already told you how you ought to arrange your life."

With equal hypocrisy, the psychiatric board that interviews him insists that the hospital is giving treatment. It then looks for signs of "illness" in Shimanov to justify his continued institutionalization.

AFTER A few days, on 5 or 6 May, there was another doctor's round. This time during the rest hour. Herman Leonidovich came up to my bed, and touching my shoulder, said:

"Well, how are things? Have you been thinking over what I said? In a few days there will be a discussion about what to do with you— whether to discharge you or give you treatment. Personally I'll insist on discharge, as I don't think any medicines will be able to change your way of thinking. But unfortunately my opinion isn't the deciding one . . ."

He was already beginning to use the familiar form of address . . . why stand on ceremony? But of course the familiarity could not be mutual: it would not be proper for me to address him, the head of the section after all, in this way. It would be imprudent. Well, well . . . I was in no situation to consider my pride, I had to get out of here . . .

"Herman Leonidovich—I have been thinking a great deal during this time about what you said to me . . . and have not been able to come to a decision easily. I cannot say that I have willingly chosen my decision; but circumstances, evidently, are such, that I am obliged to accept it. I feel that I will have to give up what you call 'religious propaganda'."

"But you understand that if you are just saying that so as to get out of here, you will turn up here again very soon?"

"Yes, I understand; and I hope I will not turn up here again".

"In that case you must repeat what you have just said, and sufficiently firmly, during the talk which you will have in a few days' time with the deputy medical director. Your wish to change your way of life may influence the decision of the doctors' council".

After a day or two I was called to Shafran's office. I went in. Shafran himself sat at the desk, and two doctors who worked under him in Section 4, Nikolai Pavlovich and Maya Merzhidovna, sat at each end of the room. There was also a middle-aged woman, unknown to me, in a white overall. I said 'Good morning' but nobody answered. The unknown woman addressed me:

"Gennady Mikhailovich, how do you explain your presence in a psychiatric hospital?

"First of all I would like to know who I am speaking to".

"The Senior Physician of Kashchenko hospital".

"Thank you. I was sent to hospital on the instructions of the KGB".

My answer did not please her.

"Who told you that it was on the instruction of the KGB?"

"They made no secret of it at the clinic".

A silence. She had nothing to use as a cover-up of course. Well, someone at the clinic would get it in the neck. Was it really permissible to be so frank? State secrets should be kept . . . Blunderers . . . They should just have sent him as quickly as possible to the hospital for us to sort out . . . They were in too much of a hurry, the slackers . . . Now the cat was out of the bag. . . And on the form sent with the patient something had been written about "religious activity" and "socially dangerous" and in the reception room remarks had been made about the KGB. Of course papers could be changed, no problem there. But then two men from the special department came to his place of work and everyone saw them—What could one do about that? Say that it was a collective hallucination? . . . Such things happen . . . All the same, what botched work . . . We study, and study, and labor and labor, and still cannot create even the appearance of legality. Disgraceful.

The senior physician asked me how I felt, and how I had been in the years since I had been in the Gannushkin Hospital; what my relationships were like in my family, at work, with my friends. Nothing to find fault with here—my relationships with everyone were good, I felt very well. It was true I did not much like living in a madhouse, but I thought that was the natural reaction of a healthy person . . .

"This is not a madhouse. It is a hospital. Before, there were madhouses where there was no treatment; but we give treatment", she answered.

"Well you are not giving me any treatment here, you know, but are just keeping me under arrest. Besides Herman Leonidovich told me that it wasn't possible to change my way of thinking with any medicines . . . Medical science has not reached that far, yet".

Herman Leonidovich fidgeted in his armchair. Ah, Herman Leonidovich! See how familiarity with patients gets you into the soup. Now you are forced to blush . . .

The conversation was clearly departing from its prearranged course. But there would be no sense in my being stiff-necked, either. On the contrary, I ought to show that I was somewhat cowed.

"Tell us, please, how it was that you came to believe in God?"

And once again I repeated my story.

Those who have had occasion to be in madhouses or psychiatric hospitals know that the doctors in them are a clever lot: you have to watch your step with them. A moment's carelessness, the slightest tendency to indulge in confidences—and wham! aha! You're caught!—and it's down on paper. They paint you up in such colors that your own mother would not recognize you. And what they write down, of course, is there for keeps. But I had already been mixed up with psychiatry once before, and there was nothing for me to hide. I tried only to give my answers accurately to the questions that interested them, and in a way that ignorant minds could understand. "Accurately"—because they were ready to seize on any word, any sentence, if it could possibly, even with a little straining, be interpreted as a sign of illness. I was speaking to them about things for them incomprehensible, about the meaninglessness of life with God deleted from it, about its tragedy—and in the eyes of the doctors I caught a certain interest . . . could not all that be interpreted as a disintegration of the consciousness? (See any psychiatric textbook). In order to explain what I meant, I began to speak of Shakespeare, Tolstoy, Dostoevsky and Pushkin. The doctors frowned: that was not "it" . . . They asked questions in which it was easy to see a simple-minded desire to hear and record that "it" of which I was devoid and which my doctors were trying so hard to foist upon me. Throughout these conversations I had an almost physical sensation that they were straining in a desire to squeeze me into a pattern understood by them, and that I was not fitting into it, and did not want to fit into it, because it was not made for me, and that this somehow made the doctors irritated inwardly, as happens with any work that does not turn out properly . . . But all the same they were cooking up some legend or

198

other about me, that was quite clear. Otherwise what sort of patient was I, and they—what sort of doctors?

So we exhausted the subject of my conversion to faith. The senior doctor went on to ask if I had services at home.

"No," I answered. "Only the usual family prayers".

But where had they got this information from? Had they been questioning neighbors, or had there been eavesdroppers under the windows? . . . Alla and I like to sing "Our Father", "The symbol of faith", "Behold Christ's resurrection", "I have no other help but Thee" and other Orthodox hymns—we sing them when a suitable occasion arises, or just any time—had this singing been taken for services? . . . Or . . . we have some records: Yurlov's singing old Christian hymns, the masses of Bach and Mozart . . . Perhaps they had not been able to distinguish? It was not possible after all to look in through the windows: we live on the second floor . . . but something suspicious had been heard . . . And now, perhaps, they wanted to find out exactly.

What was it that Ilf wrote in his notebooks?—Life isn't easy in a land of frightened idiots! Ah, my dear fellow! And do you think it is easy for the idiots to deal with us?

1969

45

"The Head Boy"

DONALD JOHNSON

Donald Johnson, lawyer, medical doctor, and later a Member of Parliament, suffered from "giddy turns and curious bouts of automatic talking" while staying at a hotel. The police brought him before the magistrate, and he was hustled off to a mental hospital, all the while protesting that he had been "doped." He maintains that he had been poisoned with Indian hemp.

Once at the hospital, he realizes that his business affairs need tending, and he determines to get out quickly. His cooperation with nurses and doctors pays off with release after six weeks.

A WEEK following my admission Betty came to see me during visiting hours. I have never been more pleased to see anyone in my life, for simultaneously with my illusions I had been full of very real anxiety for her. She was, I felt, in the same dreadful dangers as I was.

However, she greeted me with her sweet and charming smile:

"Hello, sweetheart. You're not insane."

"I know," I said, "I'm doped."

"Sh—sh. Don't say that here. They'll keep you here for ever. And do stop talking rubbish all the time."

"I'm not talking rubbish," I said.

"Is there anything you want?" she asked.

"Yes," I said dramatically, "I want apples. You must bring me apples—everyday—a fresh supply. You must eat apples yourself and see that Norman eats apples. Tell the family to eat apples too."

I do not normally eat apples even when they are put in front of me. An apple a day may keep the doctor away, but as a doctor myself I had scarcely bothered previously to eat an apple once in six months. But now my obsession to eat apples continued with undiminished intensity. Betty, who came to see me daily, would bring me 1 lb. to 1½ lbs. on each visit and I would consume these and be ready for more the following day. This obsession with apples continued for perhaps two weeks, at the end of which time my appetite for apples dropped to normal and has remained so ever since.

In the meantime, my Jurgenesque existence of the previous days was coming to an end and I was beginning to relate myself to my surroundings in normal fashion. For, with only two visits from Betty, I had grasped the position. I had 'come to' with a jolt. Not only was I confined to hospital, so we were given to understand, 'at the discretion of the authorities', but as a result of the certificate admitting me to hospital I had been removed from control of my affairs. I was deposed from my small empire; stripped of my position and my authority; a patient in a public mental hospital; treated as if I were a pauper and, indeed, an effective pauper without a penny to my name.

For the moment, the absurdity of the situation appealed to me so much that I laughed out loud. After all, the whole world had been given to me in these recent days, so what did I want with money?

Maybe, who knows, how long I might have remained in this elevated state? But what brought me down to earth was that Betty had no money either and was in utmost distress at this on her daily visits. The appalling fact hit me that, but for the hospitality of Brother Ken who had come to the rescue at a time of crisis, Betty would be wandering the streets in as penniless a condition as I was myself. Such little bit of money as Betty possessed was spent on buying me apples and other small requirements. She did not have a penny for anything else.

Maybe it was owing to the shock of this discovery, maybe it was owing to the apples I was still consuming, but my grandiose ideas slipped into the background for consideration at some future date. My phase of visionariness—the only phase which I have ever had in my life—was over, not to return. I was now improving rapidly in health day by day. I was getting out of bed and going for walks—under properly constituted supervision, of course. As I did so, I had ample leisure to contemplate the fantastic mediaeval situation, projected into modern day life, of which I was the victim. It was as if I had fallen from the top of a high building, through one floor after the other, until I had reached the basement where I reposed; and I had now to essay the tedious climb upwards.

I was only too appreciative of the fact that I was incarcerated in hospital under mental certification as 'a person of unsound mind'.

However, as impressions from the outside world came in on me, I began to put myself the simple alternative question.

Was I mad and everybody else sane? Or was I sane and everybody else mad?

Indeed the balance of my judgement came down somewhat heavily in favour of the latter alternative as I contemplated the situation. My family quarrelling and inciting litigation against each other; my hotel business in crisis; my affairs 'hanging fire'; myself the receptacle of the distress of my nearest and dearest when they came to see me, yet completely out of touch with my responsible advisers to help to mend matters.

To make a slip in these circumstances was not difficult. But I could not afford to make a slip.

No patient has surely been at any time more cooperative than I was during the remainder of my stay at the Hospital. Grateful and obsequious to the doctors, and respectful of their opinions even when they were twenty years my junior; obedient to the nurses; cooperative with the efforts made to distract and amuse me; I had my reward in turn in rapid promotion. First to the much-appreciated amenity of a private room, then to the Convalescent Ward—not nearly so amusing, alas, as the Refractory Ward had been! In the Convalescent Ward my latent capabilities as a Bridge player came to my rescue in a manner which I had never supposed possible. I did not feel like playing Bridge a bit, but I played so enthusiastically—as I co-operated in everything else so enthusiastically—that I won a prize. I had only one moment of revolt—that was against the well-meaning insistence of the charge nurse that I should take part in occupational therapy activities—minor carpentry and basketwork! As if I needed to indulge myself in minor carpentry and basketwork in order to take active interest in life with the problems that pressed in on me! However, even this rather tricky corner of occupational therapy was turned without real unpleasantness.

My medical attendants in their turn viewed this refractory patient that was myself in a new light of approval and gratification. From the awkward customer and prolonged mental illness that they had anticipated, here I was cured in this remarkably short space of time.

It was, superficially, at any rate, on the most cordial terms with all concerned that I left the hospital six weeks after my admission, once again in control of my destiny. Immediately prior to my discharge I was given an Intelligence Test. I was told at the end of this that I had scored the highest marks ever recorded by a patient in the hospital. I was the Head Boy, so to speak.

1950

46

"Spilled Sugar"

ANNA MARY WELLS

Feeling depressed, English professor Wells had signed herself onto the psychiatric ward of a university-affiliated general hospital. When she thought she was almost ready to leave, the doctors would not set a release date. She had been told that she could sign out when she chose, but then she couldn't find out what the procedure was.

She had been assured at the outset that there would be no repercussions from hospitalization: "The doctor who persuaded me to sign myself into the hospital was a young man I had known since his adolescence, and the line he used was to point out that the hospital would be unexampled literary material. (Well, yes and no.) He pointed out further that I would be in the psychiatric ward of a general hospital, so that everybody would presume I had a somatic illness. This wildly optimistic prediction should have alerted me more fully than it did to the risk I would be taking."

Having gained release, she experiences a certain rejection and discomfort on the part of her colleagues. She ruefully concludes, "Any former patient with a modicum of common sense and a position in life to maintain will attempt to do what Senator Eagleton attempted to do—conceal the fact of his hospitalization and minimize the severity of his illness."

ONE OF the first things I noticed about my fellow patients was the gloom and irritability of the men who were shortly to leave the hospital to go back to their old jobs or look for new ones. On the whole the patients headed for long-term hospitals seemed in better spirits than those going back to face the world, and the failed suicides were the most cheerful of all. I didn't attempt at the time to draw any generalizations about the pressures in our society which fill up our mental hospitals with dropouts of various sorts. I did, however, ask the university for a leave of absence for the second semester. I had entered the hosptial shortly before Thanksgiving expecting to leave it by the first of the year. When January 1 passed with no discharge date set, I realized that I didn't want to spend the month in a constant state of tension as to whether or not I would be able to resume work by February 1. The university then and later treated me with great generosity, as did the colleagues who had to take up the slack from my abrupt abandonment of my work. The leave of absence was granted, and I planned to spend it in travel abroad to which I had long looked forward.

Thereafter I bugged my doctor to set a discharge date so that I could make firm reservations. His refusal, or perhaps I should say his evasion of my questions, indicated more clearly than anything which had yet happened the enormous gulf between the patient in a psychiatric ward and a medical or surgical one. If I'd had a broken leg or a malignant fever I could have expected an explanation of the course of my recovery and at least a tentative prediction as to when I would be able to resume work. As it was, I was answered rather as if I'd been a feeble-minded child. "What's the trouble, don't you like it here? Aren't we treating you well?"

The fact that I didn't insist on a sensible answer was perhaps in itself a symptom, but whether of illness or a reaction to the treatment would be hard to say. By early January I seemed to myself to be entirely well, and the fact that the doctors apparently didn't agree with me first angered and then frightened me. The only explanation I was vouchsafed was that a clinical depression differs from a normal one in that the patient is not able to judge the state of his own feelings. If I felt elated I was merely masking my depression. No suggestion was ever offered as to how I might be able to judge for myself the state of my own mental health. The idea that I could assess it only by the reactions of others has been on the whole an injurious one over these subsequent years.

I began checking with relatives and friends in other states about what my status would be if I left without permission. These telephone calls had to be made surreptitiously while I was out on leave for an afternoon. There was one telephone on the ward to which patients had access, but it could not be used for long-distance calls and was seldom free. Moreover it was located directly across from the nurse's station where all conversations could be overheard, and their content frequently appeared on the reports to the doctors.

I had very little cash on hand for long-distance calls from pay phones, since most of my money had been turned over to the hospital for safe-keeping, but I managed two or three. They scared me worse than I was scared already. Nobody had much information, but the opinions were unanimous: you'd better stay where you are until the doctors are ready to discharge you. They must know best. I had been perfectly competent to sign myself in, but apparently nobody believed I was fit to sign myself out. I began to feel claustrophobic although the ward door always stood wide open to avoid just that effect. (It was also in full view of the nurse's station.)

I determined not to return to the hosptial from my next leave. The coincidence that served primarily to change my mind was one I would never have dared to use in fiction. I left the hospital early in the morning, luxuriated over a breakfast in the railroad station not nearly as good as the one I could have had in the hospital, but I chose it, ordered it, paid for it, and nobody minded how much I ate of it. I took a window seat on the train, and the young woman who sat down beside me confided that she was in unusually high spirits because her husband had just received the assignment he wanted as a medical resident for the next year. It was in the ward from which I thought of myself rather melodramatically as escaping. I felt only a very small passing temptation to say: 'How odd! I'm a fugitive from there.' I could imagine how her face would change if I should. I was back in the world in which shameful secrets are decently veiled, and I was beginning to learn the weight of my own.

I conferred with several other people whose judgment I respected and compromised with my original intention by returning late to the hospital after keeping an engagement with a friend. This precipitated a fuss reminiscent of boarding school days, but at least it secured me a firm date for discharge. I was told that it was a week later than it would have been had I behaved myself properly.

A few months after my discharge I stood on the Greek island of Kos in the ruins of what purported to be a mental hospital established by Aesculapius. The guide pointed out faint traces of corridors in which, he said, lions and tigers had been set free to roam as a form of shock therapy. I thought: now, there's something our doctors didn't try! I suppose if too many patients got eaten up Aesculapius abandoned the plan and advised his pupils against it.

I went back to work in the fall feeling fine, although I've never been able to decide whether the improvement was due to the therapy or the travel. The realization of how heavily I had handicapped myself came very slowly. I tried at first—for some time in fact—to follow the advice about openness. The hospital had been a very interesting experience, and I had a sizable array of amusing anecdotes about it. Every time I tried to tell one it fell with a dull thud, or someone hastily interjected a comment designed to obscure the background. I had felt a little sorry for myself about the paucity of mail during my absence; now I discovered that the friends who knew where I was had refused to share the information or had done so only with the warning that it must go no further.

There was never any question about my being taken back into the college. I had tenure, but beyond that the university was generous and the views of my colleagues on the subject of mental illness informed and liberal. I had been serving on the College Council and had not been replaced during my absence, so that my term had still one year to run. We met once weekly for a full morning and always had a coffee break in the middle. On my first morning back I spilled the sugar. Nobody laughed; nobody made a comic remark about my awkwardness; everyone pretended to ignore the accident, and I realized that they half expected me to toss the sugar bowl out the window or pour my coffee on top of the mess I had made. None of them had seen me in the hosptial passing punch and cookies with complete savoir faire.

It was the first of dozens, perhaps hundreds, of such incidents, in all of which my friends and colleagues conducted themselves with such courtesy, consideration, and kindness that I was helpless.

A year or two later I published my first article about the hospital, an account of some amateur theatricals in which I had participated. It drew a gratifying amount of attention, including a number of letters from former patients, but of friends and colleagues who mentioned it to me 95 percent spoke of my courage rather than my literary skill. I have not yet used the experience in fiction. It's hard to say why not; for one thing the hospital and my fellow patients were so different from their fictional stereotypes that any attempt to write about them tends to become expository.

After my term on the College Council expired I was not again appointed to an important committee, even though I never again spilled the sugar. There were no further promotions in rank. My teaching duties were not curtailed; no one any longer considers undergraduate teaching an important part of a college professor's work. For whatever it was worth, my own feeling was that I was a better teacher after my illness than before.

What bothered me more was a slowly growing recognition that the services I contributed to various unpopular causes were less valued (less valuable?) than they had previously been. I am afraid I had already acquired a reputation as a do-gooder; now I was regarded as a futile one whom the opposition need not take seriously. This became clear in all sorts of ways as subtle as the failure to laugh when I spilled the sugar. What people said about me almost never got back to me directly; I did hear that when I got involved in a silly and childish squabble over a faculty show of which I was co-author, my point was defused by the word which spread through the cast: 'She was in a mental hospital, you know.' If the same thing happened in more important controversies I could only suspect it.

1965

47

"Too Sick for
This Kind of Work"

GEORGE S. GLASS

When three attendants became inmates on the psychiatric service on which they had been working at a military hospital, other staff members at first could not conceive of them as patients. But they made the transition "from person into patient" (the title of Bart Smith's 1963 book), in about four weeks. In fact, as the time for release came, their former colleagues found them "too sick for this kind of work." They had taken on the stigma of mental patienthood and were now rejected by the very people who, according to mental health ideology, should accept them because they understood them. Even in the hospital setting, as Glass so trenchantly observes, ". . . psychiatric patienthood is irrevocably associated with weakness and failure. Hospitalization is seen as a permanent stigma or blemish on one's record."

BY THE end of the major part of hospitalization, when it was time to make plans for disposition and discharge, difficulties arose again once it became apparent that in fulfilling their patient roles, the ex-staff members were recovering. Their past roles as staff members again became important. The staff worked diligently to keep the ex-staff in their patient roles, refused to see them as completely well or even much improved, and focused on the "unresolved problems," their long-standing "character pathology," and even the bizarre symptoms they had demonstrated while newcomers. Their illnesses became the central focus of most discussions and conferences, and each staff member tried to reconfirm to others how the patient was still "too sick for this kind of work."

While these patients did not want to return to psychiatric work in that facility, the staff's unwillingness to consider accepting them back implies that once someone has been labeled as a patient, and been perceived and related to in the patient role, it is hard for those in opposing roles to allow him to revert to his original role. Undoubtedly, reversing roles twice in the same setting is even more difficult than the initial reversal. The staff's reluctance arose in part from their knowledge of the individual's past vulnerability, and in part from their embarrassment at having publicly seen his psychopathology. His status was also a reminder of their own vulnerability.

The patients themselves were eager to leave the hospital, thought their stay would have been shorter somewhere else, and resented hospitalization in their old unit. This was expressed by one patient, who was eager to be transferred to a VA hospital and to "be treated for myself and work my way out on my own merits."

Whether any of these patients could have successfully returned to their old job after hospitalization is uncertain, but none could have without peer support. Both the staff members and the patient felt awkward about having experienced role reversal and tended to avoid each other.

One patient did return to duty, but on a medical service. She occasionally sought out old associates on the psychiatry staff, but always felt the relationship was strained, as "I had to prove myself. Show them I was different from the way I was before and during my hospitalization. I was never relaxed." Another patient who remained in the area after discharge would occasionally return to the ward, but only to see other patients.

The staff, feeling awkward, threatened, and somewhat guilty about these patients, avoided them even when they were old friends. A senior aide who had been close to one patient before hospitalization said, when interviewed, "How is he doing? I have his phone number but feel sort of funny about calling him. It reminds me, when I was a student my best friend flipped out, and people kept asking me how he was and how I was. Kind of like they thought I might be next."

c. 1974

48

"Imbalanced"

ELOISE DAVENPORT

Ever since she had fallen on the concrete walk, Mrs. Davenport had suffered back pain. Also, she was disturbed by marital problems, neighborhood gossip, and "unpleasant symptoms associated with menopause." For these reasons she decided to enter a private mental hospital and was given electric and insulin shock during her short stay there. Ten months later she was nervous and depressed and still had persistent back pain, but not her other complaints. An orthopedist could find nothing wrong with her back. He referred her to a psychiatrist, who called in a Doctor Stewart (all names are fictitious), who convinced her to enter the private mental hospital where he worked, "Wright's Clinic." Upon release, Mrs. Davenport was referred to a psychiatrist in her home town, and he sent her to the local medical hospital for more electric shock before starting therapy.

Still plagued by back pain, possibly aggravated by the trauma of electric shock, she consulted a neurosurgeon, Dr. Barkley. Skeptical when he heard that Mrs. Davenport had been in a mental hospital, Barkley became even more doubtful on learning that her back hurt all over rather than in just one place. The fact that chiropractic adjustments had once helped her decided his diagnosis. He told her the pain was "psychosomatic" after a cursory physical examination. Mrs. Davenport went to another specialist, who repeated the medical farce.

Despairing over her status of "ex-mental patient," she surreptitiously had a urinalysis that revealed a kidney infection that may well have contributed to her back pain and that cleared up under medication. Not until she saw a physiotherapist, Dr. Denley, was the physical cause of her discomfort discovered. Following his corrective measures, Davenport's back trouble disappeared, and her emotional state improved simultaneously.

211

A British committee of inquiry reports a similar instance of deplorable misdiagnosis: "A woman was admitted to the hospital and diagnosed as an hysteric. She complained of a pain in her back. E.C.T. was ordered for her. She was unwilling to have this and she was carried struggling by several nurses and porters to the ward for E.C.T. Following administration of E.C.T. she continued to complain of pain in her back. This was investigated and she was found a have a broken back sustained prior to admission by falling down the stairs at home. This woman had been given E.C.T. while her back was broken." She died a few days later ". . . from a combination of a tumour of the corda equina, metastases and two collapsed vertebrae."[1]

DR BARKLEY, a neuro-surgeon, practised in a city about two hundred miles away. I called and made an appointment.

When I visited Dr. Barkley his first question was, "Who referred you?"

"No one."

"Why did you come to me?"

"You operated on a neighbor of mine, Mrs. Smith, who had a ruptured disk."

He nodded.

"She said you were good. I've been having back trouble, and I thought you might help me," I explained.

"Who do you want me to send your report to?"

"Do you have to send it to someone?"

"Yes, it is generally done. Who is your doctor?"

"The only doctor I'm seeing now is Dr. Catrilla, a psychiatrist in Jordontown. You can send my report to him."

Dr. Barkley looked at me as if he were seeing me for the first time.

"You're under Dr. Catrilla's care now?"

"Yes."

"You're nervous?"

"Yes . . . extremely nervous."

"What makes you nervous?"

"I've been nervous ever since I fell on a concrete walk and injured my back. That's almost four years ago. I've had shock treatments twice since then."

"You've had two shock treatments?"

"No. I've had a series of shock treatments two different times."

Dr. Barkley looked startled. He looked at me again . . . closely. Then he shrugged.

"I went to St. Joseph's about sixteen months ago. They gave me a series of electric shock and insulin treatment," I explained. "Then I was in Wright's Clinic about six months ago. After I left there I had to have electric shock treatments again. Dr. Catrilla gave them to me."

"You were in Wrights Clinic at Trentonville?"

"Yes."

"What did they tell you?"

"They said the pains in my back were psychosomatic. They said my troubles were causing my back to hurt."

"What are your troubles?"

Briefly, I recited the problems I had when I entered Wright's Clinic. Dr. Barkley shook his head.

"But those problems have cleared up. They don't bother me any more," I explained. "I don't repress my feelings anymore either."

"Are you happy now . . . since your problems have cleared up, as you say, and you don't repress your feelings?"

"No. I'm not happy," I replied, shaking my head. "I'm still nervous. And I stay so depressed."

Dr. Barkley looked solemn and shook his head.

"Tell me about your back. Where does it hurt?"

"It hurts all over . . . from top to bottom."

Dr. Barkley looked more solemn. He shook his head again.

"Have you ever been to any other doctor about your back?"

"Yes. I've been to two orthopedists and one chiropractor."

"What did they say?"

"The orthopedists said I had one leg three-eights of an inch shorter than the other, and advised me to raise the right heels of my slippers three-eights of. an inch. The chiropractor said I was out of adjustment."

"Did he give you adjustments?"

"Yes."

"Did they help you?"

"They helped . . . temporarily. But the pain always came back."

Dr. Barkley was shaking his head.

"Well, I'll take a look at your back."

He buzzed for the nurse. When she entered the room, he said, "Get Mrs. Davenport ready for an examination."

213

I disrobed, keeping nothing on but a half slip. Then the nurse helped me climb on the high table that was in the corner of the room.

"Lie flat on your back," she admonished as she placed a large cloth across my chest. Then she called Dr. Barkley into the room.

Dr. Barkley pulled down the top of my slip and pressed on my stomach.

"Does that hurt?"

"No."

He removed the cloth. Gingerly, he placed his fingertips around my breasts and under the pits of my arms.

"Now sit up," he said. "And hang your legs over the end of the table."

I did as he directed.

Dr. Barkley walked to the end of the table, and picked up a small rubber hammer from a tray. He tapped each of my knees with the hammer. They jerked when he tapped.

"Now let's take a look at that back."

He walked to the side of the table and gazed at my back.

"You have a beautiful back, Mrs. Davenport . . . so nice and smooth. I wish I had a back like that."

Nodding to the nurse, he said, "That's all. She can get dressed." He left the room.

After I had dressed, Dr. Barkley came back into the room.

"Sit down, Mrs. Davenport."

I sat down. He sat at his desk.

"Now, I'm going to be perfectly frank with you," he said. "I think it is best that you know the truth—and face it."

"Thank you, Dr. Barkley." I nodded. "I want the truth. That's why I came to you."

I waited expectantly.

"There is nothing wrong with your back," Dr. Barkley said, slowly shaking his head. "You didn't hurt it when you fell. You did absolutely nothing to your back."

"But I did!" I protested. "I never had a backache in all my life—until I fell. My back has hurt ever since. I know I hurt it."

"No, Mrs. Davenport," Dr. Barkley asserted calmly. "If you had hurt your back, it would hurt in one place—where you hurt it."

"Well, my back doesn't hurt in one place," I said. "It hurts all over."

"You might as well face it, Mrs. Davenport. You are using your back as an escape."

I stood up. "Should I pay you or the nurse?"

"You can pay the nurse . . . she's just outside."

"Thank you, Dr. Barkley. . . ."

Dr. Denley was measuring my legs and I was lying flat on my back on a table when I decided to mention something that had disturbed me for some time.

"Dr. Denley," I said, "will you please look at my hip bones? There's something I want to ask you about them"

I pulled down my half slip.

Dr. Denley had walked to the center of the table and was looking at my hips.

"Do you see how the right bone sticks up . . . as though I were skinny on that side?" I asked, nodding toward my right hip. "Now look at this left bone. It fits down smoothly. Do you see the difference?"

Dr. Denley studied my hip bones carefully. Then he ran his hand over each of them.

"Yes, I do see the difference, Mrs. Davenport." He nodded emphatically. "I certainly do!"

"Well, I've thought there was something wrong there for some time," I said. "But I always hesitated to mention it."

"Stand up," Dr. Denley requested. "And pull your shoulders back."

I stood with my shoulders pulled back while he studied my torso.

"Now relax. Stand perfectly straight, but relax. And let your arms hang loosely at your sides."

I did as he requested.

"Yes, I see your back weakness too," Dr. Denley observed. "Your spine has curved, and your right shoulder is lower than the other. Now turn around."

I turned around.

"Relax. Let your arms hang loosely at your sides."

I followed his directions. He ran his fingers across my left collar bone, then my right one.

"Yes," he nodded. "This right collar bone is lower than the other." He shook his head.

"No wonder you have a backache, Mrs. Davenport."

I smiled. I had never felt so relieved in all my life.

"When you fell you knocked your hips out of place," he explained. "That right hip has been knocked forward. That's what makes your right leg three-eighths of an inch shorter."

"And my right leg isn't really shorter than the other?" I asked. "It's just my hip being out of place that makes them uneven."

"That's it," Dr. Denley said. "And your right hip is also at an inner angle. Instead of running parallel to the other hip, it is at an angle."

I could only stare at him in wonder—and relief.

"All this damage did not happen suddenly," Dr. Denley continued. "Great damage was done, of course, when you fell. But it has taken years to get your spinal column in the shape it's in!"

"I carried my little boy so much of the time on my right hip—even after I fell," I said. "With the muscles so weak that probably pressed the hip in even more at an angle."

"You should not lift anything heavy," Dr. Denley admonished. "Your hips and entire spinal column are out of alignment. Your spine has curved, and one shoulder is lower than the other. It isn't enough to be noticed by a casual observer, but the constant pull of the muscles is enough to keep you tired all the time."

I nodded.

"It hasn't affected your posture," he continued. "That is one of the first things I noticed about you. Your posture is very good. Most people would have given in to that constant pull and slumped by now."

"What can be done for my back, Dr. Denley?" I asked.

"The important thing is to build up those muscles. Continue to wear your heels built up, and concentrate on building up your muscles. If the muscles are strong they will help hold the bones in place and keep them from pressing on the nerves."

"What should I do to build them up?"

"Rest and exercise," advised Dr. Denley. "You should take diathermy treatments, too, in order to relax the muscles. Relaxation, Mrs. Davenport, is very important. You should relax as much as possible."

Understanding the nature of my back injury was a great relief. When you have constant pain, which cannot be explained, you sometimes get to thinking that you have some weird disease . . . unknown to medical science. At least, that's what I had begun to think.

c. 1957

49

"The Insanity Bit" (II)

SEYMOUR KRIM

Krim is disappointed that even his literary and artistic friends apply old conceptions of insanity to his patienthood. Krim's "The Insanity Bit" is probably the most insightful piece in the mental hospital literature. (See the Admission section for Part I.)

In Part III, which does not appear here, Krim discusses the importance of the artist's trusting his individual experience in the face of worldly-wise and psychiatric judgments.

I RETURNED downtown—to the very Village that I heard the psychiatrist place deep in Freudian Hell, with that pious over-extension of terminology which reveals a limited private morality behind the use of so-called scientific language—and tried to tenderly pick up the threads of my former social life. I saw that my closest and most brilliant friends did not really understand, or were afraid to understand, the contemporary insanity bit. Almost all of them had been soul-whirled by psychotherapy at some time, and each had the particularly contemporary fear of insanity which has become the psychological H-bomb of city life; in theory they may have granted that insanity was no longer the uniform horror it seems to the inexperienced imagination—like a spook in the night—but centuries of inherited fear, plus the daily crises of 1950's living, made them emotionally cautious about seeing my experience as merely an *extension* of their own.

One, a poet-philosopher whom I admire, clapped me on the back and said with some literary awe that I had "returned from the dead, like Lazarus." This struck me as greatly melodramatic, untruthful, and saddening because intellectuals and especially artists should be the very people to understand that insanity today is a matter of definition, not fact; that there can no longer be a fixed criterion, just as there is no longer a reality like that described by Allen Ginsberg in "Howl" (an exciting achievement), where he sees "the best minds of my generation destroyed by madness."

I believe this is lurid sentimentality. Ginsberg may have seen the most gifted people of his generation destroyed by an *interpretation* of madness, which is a much more real threat in a time of such infinite, moon-voyaging extension to experience that the validly felt act is often fearfully jailed in a windowless cell of definition by hard-pressed authorities, whose very moral axis is in danger of toppling. Madness today is a literary word; insanity is a dated legal conception as rigid as an Ibsen play; and "psychosis," the antiseptic modern word that sends chills down the ravines of my friends' minds, has become so weakened (despite its impressive white-jacketed look) by narrow-minded, square, and fast-slipping ideological preconceptions that it must be held at arm's length, like a dead rat, for any cool understanding. When this is done, I believe you will see that the word and state of mind it tries to fix are subject to the gravest questioning; much of which centers around the amount of freedom either permitted to human expression, or more important, what it must take for itself to live in this time when such *unfamiliar* demands are made on the being. Norms crack when they can no longer fight back the content that spills over cookie-mold conceptions of "sane" behavior—and they must be elasticized to stretch around the new bundle of life.

Two weeks before I was back walking down 8th Street a gratefully free neurotic, I had been thought of in the minds of compassionate but uninformed friends as a fairly wild-eyed psychotic. The mere fact that I had been in a sanitarium had pulled a curtain of emotional blindness down over my friends' vision; and yet I was the same person I had been when I entered the happy-house. The unexamined fear of an "insanity" which no longer exists as a framed picture conventionalizes the very people who should view this now only *symbolic* word with clear, unafraid, and severely skeptical eyes. I had not been among "the dead"—unless killing time looking at "Gunsmoke" and Jackie Gleason on TV, playing bridge, and reading Tolstoy and Nathanael West is considered death. I had not been "destroyed by madness," Mr. Ginsberg!—in fact, the act of incarceration made me realize how significant (indeed indelible) individual freedom is, and thus helped brick-and-mortar my point of view rather than destroy it. When I was once again semi-knit into a way of life in my new Village home, I discovered that other writers and intellectuals whom I knew had also undergone the sanitarium or mental-hospital holiday, but had kept mum because of indecision as to how frankly one should confess such a stigma.

I understand their practical caution, but discovered that they lived in a sewer-light of guilt, fear and throat-gagging anxiety, instead of openly and articulately coping with the monster of doubt. "Do you think I'm sane? is the question I ultimately began to hear from these brilliant people (one scarred tribesman to another!) who had been intimidated into denying the worth of their most pregnant ideas, the very ones that create *new concrete standards of sanity* or *sense* in a time that has emotionally, if not yet officially, out-lived the abstractions of the past. For myself—although uncertain as to how expressive I should be, even with the very intellectuals I had always considered my brothers in a completely free inquiry into every nook and cranny of life—the problem was suddenly answered when a gifted young writer told a charming hostess I had just met that I had been in "two insane asylums."

I was pierced and hurt, not because I actually considered my supposed nuttiness a yellow badge of dishonor, but because the writer in question had ducked out from under his own experience (which I instinctively knew included some of the crises which had launched me upon the streets like a human missile) and pretended such melodrama was foreign to him. I was appalled because I thought that of all people my fellow highbrow writers should be the first to understand and concede the universal nature of the blows that had felled me in the eyes of official society. But I was wrong. There are spikes on the truth which are so close to the slashed heart of contemporary mortality that men and women will lie and refuse acknowledgement, even when it is necessary to the survival of others; they forfeit their humanhood and final worth of life by doing this, but even in the small band of the avantgarde the pursuit of the truth is given up with that weak excuse: "a practical sense of reality."

After this turncoat put-down by a member of my own club, so to speak, there was no longer any issue for myself. I could not live with the squirming burden of secretiveness because my personal history had become public gossip in the small Village group I traveled with. After snakebitten laughter at my own romantically cultivated simplemindedness in thinking my fall would be taken with the hip sophistication I had truly expected, I was glad I had become a stooge or victim; because I basically knew that I had played a juicy part in a contemporary American morality play that is going to do standing-room nightly until its implications are understood. We live in what for the imaginative person are truly hallucinated times, because there is more life on every side—and the possibility of conceiving this surplus in a dizzying multitude of ways—than our inheritance and equipment enables us to deal with. My type and perhaps your type of person only *acted out* what other less passionate people feel, but do not express. A "breakdown" such as mine can therefore be learned from:

The first thing one can see is that the isolating of a person saves his or her friends and family from being embarrassed (trivial as this seems, it is a nasty factor in institutionalization), perhaps hurt, and theoretically stops the "sick" person from doing something irreparable while in the grip of the furies. Seen this way, the enforced shackling of an individual seems sad but reasonable. But contemporary adults, however disturbed (often with justice!), are not children; there is doubt in my mind whether we have any right, other than blunt self-interest, to impose our so-called humanitarian wishes on another to the degree where we jail them in order to save them. I must illustrate this with my own case. When I was considered out of my mind during my original upward thrust into the sheer ecstasy of 100 per cent uninhibitedness, I was aware of the "daringness" of my every move; it represented at heart an existential *choice* rather than a mindless discharge. It could not be tolerated by society, and I was punished for it, but my "cure" was ultimately a chastisement, *not a medical healing process.* In my own exhibitionistic and self-dramatizing way, when I flipped, I was nevertheless instinctively rebelling against a fact which I think is objectively true in our society and time: and that is the lack of alignment between an immense inner world and an outer one which has not yet legalized, or officially recognized, the forms that can tolerate the flood of communication from the mind to the stage of action.

Traditionally, it was always taught that the artistic person could work out his or her intense private life by expressing it on the easel or typewriter. In faded theory this seems reasonable, but with the billionaire's wealth of potential human experience both fore, aft and sideways in the world today, it is abnormal not to want to participate more Elizabethanly in the over-abundant life. The hunchbacked joy the artist once may have had in poring over the objects of his interest, and then putting the extract into his work, can no longer be honestly sufficient to the most human hearts today. There has arisen an overwhelming need for the highly imaginative spirit (based on the recognition that the mere mind of man can no longer lock up the volume of its experience) to forge a bridge so that the bursting galaxy of this inner world can be received in actual public life. But there is such a time-lag between our literally amazing subjective life—which has conceptions of a powerful altitude equal to the heaven-exploring freedom of privacy—and the mummery of outer behavior, that when the contemporary imaginator expresses his genuine thoughts in public, he often feels that he has exposed himself beyond redemption. Room has not yet been made by those who dominate social power for the natural outward show of the acrobatic thinking that ceaselessly swings in the surrealistic minds of our most acute contemporaries. Put crudely but simply, a bookish notion of what constitutes "normality" in this supremely a-normal age drives the liveliest American sensibilities back into the dungeon of self—creating pressures which must maim the soul one way or another—rather than understanding that the great need today is for imagination to come gloriously out in the open and shrink the light-years that separate the mind from external life. (Trying to fill this need is, hands-down, one of the significant accomplishments of the beats—in my opinion—no matter what defensive moralists say; the raw junk that they have peddled occasionally under a Kotex flag of liberation is a different matter, which doesn't rightly fit in here.)

It was trying to close this distance between Me and Thou, between the mind and externality, that I was instinctively attempting when I cut loose with my natural suffocating self in 1955 upon the taboo ground of outer life. I could stand unfulfilled desire no longer. Thus it is my conviction today that ideals of social behavior must squat down and broaden to the point where they can both absorb and see the necessity for "aberrations" that were once, squarely and Teddy Rooseveltianly, regarded as pathological. The imagination of living human beings, not dead gods, must be openly embodied if there is to be some rational connection between what people actually are and what they are permitted to show. But as with every significiant change in meaning, such acts of expressiveness will cost blood before they will be tolerated and understood by psychiatrists, sociologists, the law, police, and all other instruments of social force. Ironically, it is the very "psychotics" in institutions who have unwittingly done the most to initiate a bigger and more imaginative conception of what constitutes *meaningful* behavior. By dealing with people imprisoned in this category, the most perceptive laymen and psychiatrists are beginning to see symbolic meanings where before they saw flat irrationality, because their approach was literal (as if anyone who had the imagination to go "mad" would be stuffy enough to act in prose!). It is then borne in upon them, out of common sense and humility, that a much more expanded conception of what is "sane" is a prerequisite to doing justice to the real emotional state of human beings today; not the abstract theorems of a clean Euclidian conception, but the real, harsh, multiple, often twisted, on-again, off-again mishmash of the so-called normal mind. One can say without pretense that the pioneering "psychotic" is the human poet of the future; and the most imaginative, least tradition-bound psychiatrists are now playing the role of New Critics, learning to closely read the difficult and unexpected meanings of what formerly were thought of as obscure— in fact off-limits—warpings of humanity.

1955

50

"Institutionalism"

JOHN NEARY

Having been in mental hospitals himself, Jack McCabe became interested in the plight of his Uncle Ken, who had been in state institutions for twenty-nine years. The hospital was willing to release the older man if he had a place to go, so McCabe and wife Carrie took him into their home. Uncle Ken adjusted well to some situations, such as eating out and shopping, but he was shy on the telephone and reluctant to go out by himself—and he balked at getting a job. McCabe and others eventually help him overcome his institutionalization.

MCCABE SWUNG into the huge parking lot and they walked together into the Sears store, heading first for the shoe department. To McCabe's surprise, the old man zeroed in on a pair of desert boots. He put them on and walked to the mirror with undisguised delight, leaving his scuffed black work brogans lying beside the box in dowdy abandonment. They moved to the hat counter and Ken matched his jaunty new footwear with a glen plaid snap-brim that might have been fashionable a decade before. The old man loved the hat at first sight and although they looked through the other stacks, that was the one he wore out of the store. First, however, they got him some socks and underwear and, passing the eyeglass counter, they got his frames adjusted so that, for the first time in years, his spectacles did not slip down the bridge of his nose. As he had in the restaurant, McCabe marveled privately at Ken's aplomb. Remembering his own acute unease after coming out of the hospital, he wondered if the old man were really as calm as he appeared or whether inwardly he felt tense and self-conscious. McCabe could not tell. There was not a sign that

223

Ken had not been shopping in crowded, busy department stores all his life.

For all his spiffy new duds, Ken was not eager to explore the town, or even the neighborhood around the McCabe home. Instead, day after day, he followed the same unvarying routine, settling into a chair in the corner of the livingroom shortly after breakfast, there to spend the morning reading the *Times*, or magazines, listening to his transistor radio, the earpiece either in his ear or dangling from his shirt pocket. He never came to the table unless he was explicitly invited—the general call, "Dinner's ready," was apparently not interpreted by Ken as having been intended to include him. At the table, he never asked for anything, but waited until he was served or offered something.

He loved to shoot pool, but he never proposed a game. Once actually in the basement, however, his cue in hand, Ken stalked the table like a grey-haired automaton, shooting with stiffly bending rigidity, attempting the most incredible shots, full-table banks, odd caroms—and more often than not he made them. McCabe asked Ken where he had learned to shoot pool and his uncle could not recall. He had never, he said, played billiards, yet he shot pool as though he had. Pool games were the only occasions when Ken allowed himself to express an opinion. "Darn!" he would declare, in a hoarse half-whisper, whenever he blew a shot, which was not often.

In fact, the pool table was the only area—forty and one-half square feet, to be exact—of life in which Ken was not self-deprecating, humble, shy, or any of the other abnegating qualities he otherwise was. The same man who had the audacity to attempt a full-table bank shot—the physical equivalent of trying to hit an elevator button with a Ping-Pong ball from eighteen feet away—when the outcome of the game depended on his making it, literally shuddered at the thought of walking to the mail box a block and a half from the front door. Dialing the telephone caused Ken's hand to shake and his voice to quaver and it was with audible tremulous relief that Ken said thanks profusely to the recorded voice of the weather girl. Ken would admit to no trepidation. Nothing looked different to him, he said; everything seemed just the way it had before he went into the hospital. Nonetheless, McCabe's second-oldest child had to take Ken by the hand before the old man would consent to walking their bulldog around the block. When Ken finally steeled himself to walk to the Post Office and back, a distance of about two miles, he was gone so long that McCabe had dialed the police, reporting him lost.

Readjusting to life as a free man came to Ken with a glacial, nearly imperceptible slowness that left McCabe and Carrie worn and raw. Carrie was having an increasingly hard time disguising that irritation McCabe had sensed the second night Ken was with them. She was upset at how capable Ken was of merely sitting. McCabe became as concerned as she was over whether the old man was going to make it—or whether he merely saw their livingroom as another dayroom.

Dr. Olner, the psychiatrist Ken saw at a public clinic soon after he arrived in Harborview, told McCabe, "The state of Pennsylvania did a better job of brain-washing your uncle than the Red Chinese could ever do." The doctor, a young, tough-looking, tough-talking man with the build and manner of a rock-climber or a cross-country bicyclist—wiry, no-nonsense, a sound-mind-sound-body believer— explained what he meant. The decades of hospitalization had transformed Ken into a professional patient, Dr. Olner said. The condition was a definable pathology all by itself, overshadowing in the end whatever malady had made hospitalization seem necessary to begin with. The prospect of undoing the hardened accretion of those years of hospital life, of dissolving the "institutional syndrome," of eradicating the "brain-washing" effect of patienthood, was bleak. It was not hopeless. In fact, Olner reduced Ken's dosage of Thorazine (the old man could not recall how long he had been taking it—since its invention?) and said he would check around on possibilities for finding him some kind of activity.

Ken was unenthusiastic about that. In what had become their ritual conversation, he replied to McCabe's questions about desires, wishes, ambitions always with the same litany of answers: He didn't feel too well, he felt not so good today; he couldn't do anything; he didn't think he could do that particular kind of thing; he didn't really want to do anything. He might like to do office work, he admitted—but he insisted he "probably wouldn't be up to it," and McCabe and Carrie suspected Ken was stipulating something he believed he wouldn't be offered, so he could refuse everything else that fell short. McCabe would often sit in the livingroom with Ken and try to talk him out of his lethargy, facing him across the coffee table, both men with cans of beer on the floor, smoking heavily. McCabe wished he had some kind of magic feather to hand this fearful Dumbo in order to cozen him into flight. He felt guilty, as though he were prodding a weaker creature, conscious of the gap in their ages, their situations. He sat there, thirty-three years old, earning close to thirty thousand dollars a year now, his house and family around him, urging this old uncle to undertake embarking on life at an age when many men are giving serious thought to how they will spend their retirement. The evening usually ended ambiguously.

McCabe wished he had some help. Olner didn't feel more intensive therapy would accomplish anything. The rest of his family had reacted to the news that Ken was out with quiet surprise and only faint cries of joy. Ken's mother had said that she was happy and, over the phone, she thanked McCabe, her grandson, for freeing Ken. Still, even her rejoicing had been muted. Perhaps it was just shock. Another relative, however, had warned McCabe: "Don't think you're going to palm him off on us." McCabe wondered now for the first time if there might have been more behind Ken's three decades of hospitalization than only lethargy or injustice, and pondered the genuine possibility that Ken was never going to get off his ass, ever. When McCabe suggested strongly that Ken come along the next time he drove Carrie and the kids the two hundred and fifty miles to see his parents and Ken's mother, Ken demurred. He didn't feel well enough, hadn't been feeling too good, he said, in a mumble of woe. McCabe began to wonder if he were not encountering the truth of the oriental notion that saving a man's life obligates you to care for him for the rest of yours.

Enough of this bullshit, McCabe told himself time after time, and embarked on a grilling of the old man in his toughest police reporter style. Each time he pulled back because the interview obviously was not leading Ken to any epiphany of illogic but merely uncovering further the old man's unwillingness to budge. McCabe found himself shrinking from exploring this as one might avert one's gaze from a badly deformed cripple and yet find oneself covertly inspecting, searching.

1970

51

"Counting the Mad"

DONALD JUSTICE

Reacting to a plot to send him to an asylum, the Bishop in Jack London's *The Iron Heel* cries, "No! No! Not that! Not that!"[1] The parallel with this poem is striking. Justice, whose "wife once worked briefly at Rockland State but fled in tears,"[2] depicts the inmate as a human being who is entitled to human rights.

THIS ONE was put in a jacket,
This one was sent home,
This one was given bread and meat
But would eat none,
And this one cried No No No No
All day long.

This one looked at the window
As though it were a wall,
This one saw things that were not there,
This one things that were,
And this one cried No No No No
All day long.

This one thought himself a bird,
This one a dog,
And this one thought himself a man,
An ordinary man,
And cried and cried No No No No
All day long.

227

Notes

For full citations, refer to the References and Supplementary Bibliography.

ADMISSIONS INTRODUCTION

[1]Stern, 1968, p. 41.
[2]Miller, 1976, p. 12.
[3]Sheeley, 1959, p. 28.
[4]Szasz, 1966, p. 92.
[5]Larson, 1966, p. 92.
[6]Petris Committee, 1967, p. 23.
[7]Rachlin, 1975, p. 190, bracketed material added.
[8]Miller, 1976, pp. 68-69.
[9]Miller, 1976, pp. 65-68.
[10]Rappeport, 1967, p. 76.
[11]Siebert, 1968, p. 16.
[12]Arco, 1967, p. 14.
[13]Martindale, 1973, p. 191.
[14]Scheff, 1966, p. 88.
[15]Benziger, 1976, p. 101.
[16]Miller, 1976, pp. 59-65.
[17]*Dilemma,* 1967, pp. 19-20.
[18]Anon., 1839, p. 16.
[19]Grimes, 1954, p. 225.
[20]Szasz, 1971b, p. 13.
[21]Rosenberg *et al.,* 1964, p. 162.
[22]Goffman, 1961, pp. 1-124.
[23]Manfreda, 1968, p. 95.
[24]Subcommittee to Investigate the Administration, 1972, pp. 149-150.
[25]Prittie, 1964, pp. 33-34.
[26]Wertham, 1966, p. 158.
[27]Miller, 1971, pp. 22-23.
[28]Szasz, 1971a, p. 64, bracketed word added.
[29]Rock *et al.,* 1968, p. 139.
[30]Sutherland, 1977, p. 224.
[31]Rachlin *et al.,* 1975, p. 190.
[32]Peszke, 1975, p. 33.
[33]Szasz, 1970.

CHAPTER 5 (Gotkin)

[1]Dembo and Hanfmann, 1935, p. 383.

CHAPTER 12 (Olson)

[1]Gallup, 2:2, p. 320.
[2]Sutherland, 1976, epigraph.

TREATMENT INTRODUCTION

[1]Robert and Kiernan, 1969, p. 196.
[2]Torrey, 1972, p. 72.
[3]Haley, 1969, p. 132.
[4]Friedberg, 1976, p. 41.
[5]Benedek, 1965, pp. 83-84.
[6]Breggin, 1971, p. 287.
[7]Subcommittee to Investigate Juvenile Delinquency, V.II, 1977, p. 579.
[8]Benziger, 1976, p. 110.
[9]Duffy and Litin, 1967, p. 30.
[10]Friedberg, 1976, p. 32.
[11]Freeman, 1968, p. 29.
[12]Lennard *et al.,* 1971, p. 57.
[13]Glenn, 1974, p. 153.
[14]Barton, 1962, p. 220.
[15]Subcommittee to Investigate Juvenile Deliquency, V.II, 1977, p. 164.
[16]Rosenhan, 1973, p. 256.
[17]Brandt, 1975, p. 40.
[18]Rosenhan, 1973, pp. 255-256.
[19]Kalogerakis, 1971.
[20]Ekblom, 1970, p. 101.
[21]Hall *et al.,* 1952, p. 166.
[22]Goffman, 1961, p. 7.
[23]Strauss *et al.,* 1964, p. 304.

[24]Mercier, 1931, p. 230.
[25]Clark, 1964, p. 59, bracketed words added.
[26]Ayllon and Azrin, 1968, p. 1, bracketed material added.
[27]Breggin, 1974, pp. 89-95.
[28]Rosenhan, 1973, p. 256.
[29]Ishiyama *et al.,* 1967, p. 570.
[30]Rubenstein and Lasswell, 1966, p. 59.
[31]Perrucci, 1974, p. 65.

CHAPTER 17 (Weitz)
[1]Barton, 1962, p. 27.

CHAPTER 21 (West)
[1]Smith, 1945, p. 132.

CHAPTER 26 (Marks)
[1]Duffy and Litin, 1967, pp. 47-49.

CHAPTER 27 (Clark)
[1]Barton, 1962, p. 17.

CHAPTER 28 (Solomon)
[1]Personal communication, March 21, 1977.

CHAPTER 29 (Rokeach)
[1]Benedek, 1965, p. 115.

CHAPTER 32 (Fry)
[1]Barry, 1971, p. 132.

RELEASE INTRODUCTION
[1]Scull, 1977, pp. 151-153.
[2]Rock *et al.,* 1968, p. 262.
[3]Stotland and Kobler, 1965, p. 150.
[4]Rock *et al.,* 1968, p. 233.
[5]Ekblom, 1970, pp. 90-97.
[6]Raphael and Peers, 1972, p. 14.
[7]Martin, 1959, p. 23.
[8]Goffman, 1961, p. 367.
[9]Hennell, 1967, pp. 182-183.
[10]Goffman, 1963.
[11]Kramer, 1962, p. 19.
[12]Perrucci, 1974, p. 18.
[13]Duffy and Litin, 1967, p. 28.
[14]Abramowitz, 1946, p. 734.
[15]Lorand, 1970, p. 103.
[16]Lowry, 1963, p. 37.
[17]Hennell, 1967, p. 249.
[18]Donaldson, 1975.

[19]Szasz, 1977.
[20]*Ibid.,* p. 83.

CHAPTER 39 (United Press)
[1]Dees, 1950, pp. 126-127.
[2]Gould, 1974, p. 67.
[3]Freeman, 1968, pp. 281-282.
[4]McCaffrey, 1975, p. 22.

CHAPTER 48 (Davenport)
[1]Ankers, 1976, pp. 70 & 163.

CHAPTER 51 (Justice)
[1]London, 1948, p. 200.
[2]Personal communication, September 8, 1976.

References and Supplementary Bibliography

Abramowitz, Isodore. *The Great Prisoners: The First Anthology of Literature Written in Prison.* New York: Dutton, 1946.

Agel, Jerome, ed. *The Radical Therapist Collective.* New York: Ballantine Books, 1971.

Agel, Jerome, ed. *Rough Times.* New York: Ballantine Books, 1973.

Ankers, William Brian, and Olleste, Etsello. "St. Augustine's Hospital, Chartham Down, near Canterbury, Kent: A Critique Regarding Policy." In South East Thames Regional Health Authority's *Report of Committee of Enquiry St. Augustine's Hospital, Chartham, Canterbury.*

Anonymous. *On the Present State of Lunatic Asylums: With Suggestions for their Improvement.* London: Drury, 1839; quoted by Scull, 1977, p. 108.

Arco Editorial Board. *Hospital Attendant* (3rd ed.). New York: Arco, 1967.

Ayllon, Theodoro, and Azrin, Nathan. *The Token Economy: A Motivational System for Therapy and Rehabilitation.* New York: Appleton-Century-Crofts, 1968.

Barry, Anne. *Bellevue is a State of Mind.* New York: Harcourt Brace Jovanovich, 1971.

Barton, Walter E. *Administration in Psychiatry.* Springfield, Illinois: C.C. Thomas, 1962.

Becker, Howard S. *Outsiders: Studies in the Sociology of Deviance.* New York: The Free Press, 1963.

Belknap, Ivan. *Human Problems of a State Mental Hospital.* New York: McGraw-Hill, 1956.

Benedek, Istvan. *The Gilded Cage.* Budapest: Corvina Press, 1965.

Benziger, Barbara Field. *Speaking Out: Therapists and Patients—How They Cure and Cope with Mental Illness Today.* New York: Walker, 1976.

Bittner, E. "Police Discretion in Emergency Apprehension of Mentally Ill Persons." *Social Problems,* 14, pp. 278-292, 1967.

Braginsky, Benjamin M., and Braginsky, Dorothea D. *Mainstream Psychology: A Critique.* New York: Holt, Rinehart & Winston, 1974.

231

Braginsky, Benjamin M.; Braginsky, Dorothea D.; and Ring, Kenneth. *Methods of Madness: The Mental Hospital as a Last Resort.* New York: Holt, Rinehart & Winston, 1969.

Brakel, Samuel J., and Rock, Ronald S. *The Mentally Disabled and the Law* (revised ed.). Chicago: University of Chicago Press, 1971.

Brandt, Anthony. *Reality Police: The Experience of Insanity in America.* New York: Morrow, 1975.

Breggin, Peter. "Coercion of Voluntary Patients in an Open Hospital." *Archives of General Psychiatry,* 10:2, pp. 173-181, 1964.

Breggin, Peter. *The Crazy from the Sane.* New York: Lyle Stuart, 1971.

Bryan, William A. *Administrative Psychiatry.* New York: Pageant Book Company, 1958 (originally published 1936).

Byrd, Max. *Visits to Bedlam: Madness and Literature in the 18th Century.* Columbia, South Carolina: University of South Carolina Press, 1974.

Caudill, William. *The Psychiatric Hospital as a Small Society.* Cambridge: Published for the Commonwealth Fund by Harvard University Press, 1958.

Chu, Franklin D., and Trotter, Sharland. *The Madness Establishment: Ralph Nader's Study Group Report on the National Institute of Mental Health.* New York: Grossman, 1974.

Clark, David H. *Administrative Therapy: The Role of the Doctor in the Therapeutic Community.* London: Tavistock, 1964.

Dees, Jesse Walter Jr., ed. *Snake Pit Attendant: The Experiences of a Mental Hospital Attendant.* New York: Exposition Press, 1950.

Dembo, Tamara, and Hanfmann, Eugenia. "The Patient's Psychological Situation upon Admission to a Mental Hospital." *American Journal of Psychology,* 47:3, pp. 381-408, July, 1935.

Denner, Bruce, and Price, Richard, eds. *Community Mental Health: Social Action and Reaction.* New York: Holt, Rinehart & Winston, 1973.

Deutsch, Albert. *The Mentally Ill in America: A History of their Care and Treatment from Colonial Times* (2nd ed.) New York: Columbia University Press, 1949 (originally published 1938).

Donaldson, Kenneth. *Insanity Inside Out.* New York: Crown, 1976.

Duffy, John C., and Litin, Edward M. *The Emotional Health of Physicians.* Springfield, Illinois: C.C. Thomas, 1967.

Dunham, H. Warren, and Weinberg, S. Kirsone. *The Culture of the State Mental Hospital.* Detroit: Wayne State University Press, 1960.

Ekblom, Bengt. *Acts of Violence by Patients in Mental Hospitals.* Translated by Helen Frey, Sweden: Svenska Bokfoerlaget, 1972.

Ennis, Bruce. *Prisoners of Psychiatry.* New York: Harcourt Brace Jovanovich, 1972.

Ennis, Bruce, and Siegel, Loren. *The Rights of Mental Patients: The Basic*

REFERENCES AND BIBLIOGRAPHY

American Civil Liberties Union Guide to a Mental Patient's Rights. New York: Avon Books, 1973.

Freeman, Lucy. *Celebrities on the Couch: Personal Adventures in Psychoanalysis.* Los Angeles: Price Stern, 1970.

Freeman, Walter. *The Psychiatrist: Personalities and Patterns.* New York: Grune & Stratton, 1968.

Friedberg, John. *Shock Treatment is not Good for Your Brain.* San Francisco: Glide, 1976.

Gallup, Donald, "Supplementary Bibliography." *Paideuma,* 2:2, pp. 315-324. On p. 320 attributes to Pound "A Call to Fight Freudian Evil," by "An Overseas Correspondent," which appeared in the Australian *New Times,* September 21, 1956. p. 7.

Ginsberg, Allen. *Kaddish and Other Poems 1958-1960.* San Francisco: City Lights Books, 1961.

Glenn, Michael, ed. *Voices from the Asylum.* New York: Harper & Row, 1974.

Goffman, Erving. *Asylums: Essays on the Social Situation of Mental Patients and other Inmates.* New York: Doubleday, 1961.

Goffman, Erving. *Stigma: Notes on the Management of Spoiled Identity.* New Jersey: Prentice-Hall, 1963.

Gould, Miriam. "One-Way Mirror," in Hirsch et al., eds. San Francisco: Glide, 1974, p. 67.

Gralnick, Alexander. *The Psychiatric Hospital as a Therapeutic Instrument: Collected Papers of High Point Hospital.* New York: Brunner/Mazel, 1969.

Greenblatt, Milton; Levinson, David J.; and Williams, Richard H., eds. *The Patient and the Mental Hospital.* Glencoe, Illinois: The Free Press, 1957.

Grimes, John Maurice. *When Minds Go Wrong: The Truth about our Mentally Ill and their Care in Mental Hospitals.* New York: The Devin-Adair Company, 1954 (originally published 1951).

Grob, Gerald N. *Mental Institutions in America: Social Policy to 1875.* New York: Free Press, 1973.

Haley, Jay. "The Art of Being Schizophrenic," in his *The Power Tactics of Jesus and other Essays.* New York: Grossman, 1969.

Hall, Bernard; Gangemi, Mary; Litt, M.; Norris, V.L. Vail, Vivienne Hutchins; and Sawatsky, Gordon. *Psychiatric Aide Education.* New York: Grune & Stratton, 1952.

Halleck, Seymour L. *The Politics of Therapy.* New York: Science House, 1971.

Heckel, Robert V.; Perry, Charles; and Reeves, P.G., Jr. *The Discharged Mental Patient: A 5-Year Statistical Survey.* Columbia, South Carolina: University of South Carolina Press, 1973.

Hennell, Thomas. *The Witnesses.* New York: University Books, 1967 (originally published 1938).

Hirsch, Sherry; Adams, Joe Kennedy; Frank, Leonard Roy; Hudson, Wade; Keene, Richard; Krawitz-Keene, Gail; Richman, David; and Roth, Robert, eds. *Madness Network News Reader.* San Francisco: Glide, 1974.

Hollingshead, August B., and Redlich, Frederick C. *Social Class and Mental Illness: A Community Study.* New York: Wiley, 1958.

Ibsen, Henrik. *Peer Gynt,* in *The Works of Henrik Ibsen,* one volume. New York: Walter J. Black, 1928 (originally published 1867).

Ishiyama, Toaru; Batman, Robert; and Hewitt, Eileen. "Let's Be Patients." *American Journal of Nursing,* 67:3, pp. 569-571, 1967.

Joint Commission on Mental Illness and Health. *Action for Mental Health: Final Report of the Joint Commission on Mental Illness and Health.* New York: Basic Books, 1961.

Jones, Maxwell. *Beyond the Therapeutic Community: Social Learning and Social Psychiatry.* New Haven: Yale University Press, 1968.

Kalogerakis, Michael G. "The Assaultive Psychiatric Patient." *Psychiatric Quarterly,* 45:3, pp. 372-381, 1971, as summarized in *Psychological Abstracts,* #7388, p. 801, July-December, 1972.

Kittrie, Nicholas, N. *The Right to Be Different: Deviance and Enforced Therapy.* Baltimore: The Johns Hopkins Press, 1971.

Klett, Shirley L.; Berger, D.G.; Lee, G.S.; and Rice, C.E. "Patient Evaluation of the Psychiatric Ward." *Journal of Clinical Psychology,* 19:3, pp. 347-351, 1963.

Kotin, Joel, and Schur, Michael J. "Attitudes of Discharged Mental Patients toward their Hospital Experiences: A Preliminary Study." *Journal of Nervous and Mental Disease,* 149:5, pp. 408-414, 1969.

Kramer, Bernard M. *Day Hospital: A Study of Partial Hospitalization in Psychiatry.* New York: Grune & Stratton, 1962.

Larson, Willard A.E. "The Positive Self-Fulfilling Prophecy." Presented to the National Institute of Mental Health on NHO 164601, March 1966, quoted by Petris Committee, pp. 152-153, 1967.

Leifer, Ronald. *In the Name of Mental Health: The Social Functions of Psychiatry.* New York: Science House, 1969.

Lennard, Henry L.; with Epstein, Leon J.; Bernstein, Arnold; and Ransom, Donald C. *Mystification and Drug Abuse: Hazards in Using Psychoactive Drugs.* San Francisco: Jossey-Bass, 1971.

London, Jack. *The Iron Heel.* New York: Grayson, 1948 (originally published 1907).

Lorand, Sandor. "Psychoanalysts are Human, Too," in L. Freeman, *Celebrities on the Couch.* Los Angeles: Price Stern, pp. 101-116, 1970.

Lowry, Malcolm. *Lunar Caustic.* London: Jonathan Cape, 1963.

REFERENCES AND BIBLIOGRAPHY

Manfreda, Marguerite Lucy. *Psychiatric Nursing* (8th ed.). Philadelphia: Davis, 1968.

Martin, John Bartlow. *The Pane of Glass*. New York: Harper, 1959.

Martindale, Don, and Martindale, Edith. *Psychiatry and the Law: The Crusade against Involuntary Hospitalization*. St. Paul, Minnesota: Windflower, 1973.

Matthews, Arthur R., Jr. "Observations on Police Policy and Procedures for Emergency Detention of the Mentally Ill." *Journal of Criminal Law, Criminology and Police Science,* 61:2, pp. 283-295, June, 1970.

McCaffrey, Brian. Review of *Hurry Tomorrow* in *The Conspiracy,* October, 1975, quoted in *Madness Network News,* V. 3, no issue stated, p. 22.

Mee, Cornelia. *The Internment of Soviet Dissenters in Mental Hospitals*. Pamphlet, no place, no date (London, c. 1971).

Mendel, Werner M. "Dismantling the Mental Hospital," in Plog Research, Inc., and Stanford Research Institute. *"Where is My Home?" Proceedings of a Conference on the Closing of State Mental Hospitals*. Springfield, Virginia: National Technical Information Service, United States Department of Commerce, 1974, pp. 19-27.

Mercier, Charles. *Criminal Responsibility*. New York: Physicians and Surgeons, 1931 (originally published 1926).

Milford, Nancy. *Zelda*. New York: Harper & Row, 1970.

Miller, Kent S. *Managing Madness: The Case against Civil Commitment*. New York: The Free Press, 1976.

Miller, Merle. *On Being Different: What it Means to be a Homosexual*. New York: Random House, 1971.

Network Against Psychiatric Assault. *Forced Treatment Equals Torture*. San Francisco: Network Against Psychiatric Assault, no date (c. 1974).

Orlans, Harold. "An American Death Camp," in Rosenberg, *et. al., Mass Society in Crisis,* pp. 614-628. New York: Macmillan, 1964. (Originally appeared in *Politics,* 205, pp. 162-167, Summer, 1948).

Perrucci, Robert. *Circle of Madness: On Being Insane and Institutionalized in America*. New Jersey: Prentice-Hall, 1974.

Peszke, Michael Alfred. *Involuntary Treatment of the Mentally Ill: The Problem of Autonomy*. Springfield, Illinois: C.C. Thomas, 1975.

Petris Committee. *The Dilemma of Mental Commitments in California: The Final Report of the Petris Committee,* 1967 (Available on inter-library loan from the California State Library, Government Publications Section, P.O. Box 2037, Sacramento, Ca. 95809. Indicate: L500 W35 Nos. 8 & 8A).

Petrov, Vladimir. "Experimenting for the NKVD: A Prison-Camp Brigadier Learns how Soviet Psychiatrists Turn Sane Men into Gibbering Idiots." *Catholic Digest,* pp. 1421-1428, February, 1950.

235

Plath, Sylvia. *The Bell Jar.* New York: Harper & Row, 1971 (originally published 1963).

Plog Research, Inc., and Stanford Research Institute. *"Where is My Home?" Proceedings of a Conference on the Closing of State Mental Hospitals.* Springfield, Virginia: National Technical Information Service, United States Department of Commerce, 1974.

Price, Richard H. and Denner, Bruce, eds. *The Making of A Mental Patient.* New York: Holt, Rinehart & Winston, 1973.

Prittie, Terence. *Germans against Hitler.* Boston: Little Brown, 1964.

Rachlin, Stephen; Pam, Alvin; and Milton, Janet. "Civil Liberties versus Involuntary Hospitalization." *American Journal of Psychiatry,* 132:2, pp. 189-191, 1975.

Raphael, Winifred, and Peers, Valerie. *Psychiatric Hospitals Viewed by their Patients.* London: King Edward's Hospital Fund for London, 1972.

Rappeport, Jonas, ed. *The Clinical Evaluation of the Dangerousness of the Mentally Ill.* Springfield, Illinois: C.C. Thomas, 1967.

Reddaway, Peter. *Uncensored Russia: Protest and Dissent in the Soviet Union.* New York: American Heritage Press, 1972.

Reddaway, Peter. *Victims of Soviet Psychiatric Abuse Since Late 1972: A Preliminary Dossier.* New York & London: Amnesty International, 1976.

Robert, A.A., and Kiernan, Thomas. *Pictorial History of Psychology and Psychiatry.* New York: Philosophical Library, 1969.

Rock, Ronald S.; with Jacobson, Marcus A.; and Janopaul, Richard M. *Hospitalization and Discharge of the Mentally Ill.* Chicago: The University of Chicago Press, 1968.

Rosen, George. *Madness in Society: Chapters in the Historical Sociology of Mental Illness.* Chicago: University of Chicago Press, 1968.

Rosenberg, Bernard; Gerver, Israel; and Howton, F. William. *Mass Society in Crisis: Social Problems and Social Pathology.* New York: Macmillan, 1964.

Rosenhan, David Leonard. "On Being Sane in Insane Places." *Science,* 179, pp. 250-258, January, 1973.

Rothman, David J. *The Discovery of the Asylum: Social Order and Disorder in the New Republic.* Boston: Little Brown, 1971.

Rubenstein, Robert., and Lasswell, Harold. *The Sharing of Power in a Psychiatric Hospital.* New Haven: Yale University Press, 1966.

Sarbin, Theodore R., and Mancuso, James. "Failure of Moral Enterprise: Attitudes of the Public toward Mental Illness." *Journal of Consulting and Clinical Psychology,* 35, pp. 159-173, 1970.

Scheff, Thomas J. *Being Mentally Ill: A Sociological Theory.* Chicago: Aldine, 1966.

Scull, Andrew T. *Decarceration: Community Treatment of the Deviant—A Radical View.* New Jersey: Prentice-Hall, 1977.

Sewall, Lee G.; Gillen, John; and Frank, M. Le Bar. "Through the Patient's Eyes." *Mental Hygiene,* 39:2, pp. 284-292, April, 1955.

Sheeley, William. "Protecting State Hospital Function." *Mental Hospitals,* pp. 28-29, October, 1959.

Siebert, Lawrence Al. *Are We Mentally Ill? A Collection of Papers by Al Siebert.* (Oregon): Lawrence A. Siebert, 1968.

Smit, Bart. *From Person into Patient.* The Hague: Mouton, 1963.

Smith, Logan Pearsall. *All Trivia.* New York: Harcourt Brace, 1945 (anecdote originally published in 1921 in *More Trivia*).

Stanton, Alfred A., and Schwartz, Morris S. *The Mental Hospital: A Study of Institutional Participation in Psychiatric Illness and Treatment.* New York: Basic Books, 1954.

Stein, Edna, and Sorensen, Karl Dan. "A Cooperative Apartment for Transitional Patients." *Mental Hygiene,* 56:1, pp. 68-74, Winter, 1972.

Stern, Edith M., with the collaboration of Hamilton, Samuel W. *Mental Illness: A Guide for the Family* (5th ed.). New York: The Commonwealth Fund, 1968.

Stone, Michael H. "Management of Unethical Behavior in a Psychiatric Hospital Staff." *American Journal of Psychotherapy,* 29:3, pp. 391-401, July, 1975.

Stotland, Ezra, and Kobler, Arthur L. *Life and Death of a Mental Hospital.* Seattle: University of Washington Press, 1965.

Strauss, Anselm; Schatzman, Leonard; Bucher, Rue; Ehrlich, Danuto; and Sabshin, Melvin. *Psychiatric Ideologies and Institutions.* London: The Free Press of Glencoe, Collier-Macmillan Limited, 1964.

Subcommittee to Investigate the Administration of the Internal Security Act and other Internal Security Laws of the Committee on the Judiciary United States Senate. *Abuse of Psychiatry for Political Repression in the Soviet Union.* Washington, D.C.: United States Government Printing Office, 1972.

Subcommittee to Investigate Juvenile Delinquency of the Committee on the Judiciary United States Senate. *The Abuse and Misuse of Controlled Drugs in Institutions.* Washington, D.C.: United States Government Printing Office, 1977, in three volumes.

Sutherland, N.S. *Breakdown.* New York: Stein & Day, 1977.

Szasz, Thomas. *The Age of Madness: The History of Involuntary Mental Hospitalization Presented in Selected Texts.* New York: Anchor Press/Doubleday, 1973.

Szasz, Thomas. *Ceremonial Chemistry: The Ritual Persecution of Drugs, Addicts, and Pushers.* New York: Anchor Press/Doubleday, 1974.

Szasz, Thomas. "From the Slaughterhouse to the Madhouse." *Psychotherapy,* 8:1, pp. 64-67, Spring, 1971a.

237

Szasz, Thomas. *Ideology and Insanity: Essays in the Psychiatric Dehumanization of Man.* New York: Anchor Press/Doubleday, 1970.

Szasz, Thomas. "Involuntary Commitment: A Form of Slavery." *The Humanist,* pp. 11-14, July/August, 1971b.

Szasz, Thomas. *Law, Liberty and Psychiatry: The Inquiry into the Social Uses of Mental Health Practices.* New York: Macmillan, 1963.

Szasz, Thomas. *The Manufacture of Madness: A Comparative Study of the Inquisition and the Mental Health Movement.* New York: Harper & Row, 1970.

Szasz, Thomas. "Mental Illness is a Myth." *The New York Times Magazine,* pp. 90-92, June 12, 1966.

Szasz, Thomas. *The Myth of Mental Illness: Foundations of a Theory of Personal Conduct.* New York: Paul Hoeber, 1961.

Szasz, Thomas. *Psychiatric Justice.* New York: Macmillan, 1965.

Szasz, Thomas. *Psychiatric Slavery.* New York: The Free Press, 1977.

Szasz, Thomas. *Schizophrenia: The Sacred Symbol of Psychiatry.* New York: Basic, 1976.

Thorpe, E.T. "Patients' Opinion Poll." *Mental Health,* 25:4, pp. 38-39, 1966.

Torrey, E. Fuller. *The Death of Psychiatry,* Radnor, Pennsylvania: Chilton, 1974.

Torrey, E. Fuller. *The Mind Game: Witchdoctors and Psychiatrists.* New York: Emerson Hall, 1972.

Vail, David. *Dehumanization and the Institutional Career.* Springfield, Illinois: C.C. Thomas, 1966.

Vincent, M.O.; Robinson. E.A.; and Lott, L. "Physicians as Patients: Private Psychiatric Hospital Experience." *Canadian Medical Association Journal.* 100:9, pp. 403-412, March 1, 1969.

Wertham, Frederic. *A Sign for Cain: An Exploration of Human Violence.* New York: Macmillan, 1966.

Wiener, Leonard; Becker, Alvin; and Friedman, Tobias T. *Home Treatment: Spearhead of Community Psychiatry.* Pittsburgh: University of Pittsburgh Press. 1967.

Weiss, Henry H., and Pizer, Evan F. "Hospitalizing the Young: Is it for their own Good?" *Mental Hygiene,* 54:4, pp. 498-502, 1970.

Wenger, Dennis L., and Fletcher, Richard C. "The Effect of Legal Counsel on Admissions to a State Mental Hospital," in Price & Denner, 1973, pp. 135-146 (originally appeared in *Journal of Health and Human Behavior,* 10, pp. 66-72, 1969).

Zander, Alvin; Cohen, Arthur R.; Stotland, Ezra; with the collaboration of Hymovitch, Bernard, and Riedl, Otto. *Role Relations in the Mental Health Professions.* Ann Arbor: University of Michigan, The Institute for Social Research, 1957.

REFERENCES AND BIBLIOGRAPHY

Zaslove, Marshall O.; Ungerleider, J. Thomas; and Fuller, Marcelle C. "How Psychiatric Hospitalization Helps: Patient Views vs. Staff Views." *Journal of Nervous and Mental Disease,* 142:6, pp. 568-576, 1966.

Ziskin, Jay. *Coping with Psychiatric and Psychological Testimony* (2nd ed.). Beverly Hills, California: Law and Psychology Press, 1976.

Index

Adams, Sherman, 57
Admissions, 3-73; doctor-recommended, 26-29; fraud, 8-9, 69; interviews, 66-67; involuntary, 3, 4, 6, 9, 10-26, 65-66, 168-169; need for rational system, 7; police admissions, 51-52, 65-66; readmission rate, 168; social worker-petitioned, 38; voluntary, 7, 9, 40-41
Adolescents, 17-22; emotionally disturbed, 10-16, 170-175
Aesculapius, 206-207
American Association for the Abolition of Involuntary Hospitalization, 127
Anderson, Don, 41
Apathy, 84
Arnold, Thurman, 57
Artaud, Antonin, 9, 71
Attendants: abuse of patients, 79-80, 82, 92-93, 96, 112-114; guidelines, 6, 80; power, 81, 98-99; lack of personal involvement, 82, 138-139; See also Staff-patient relations

Back-warding, 81
Barbamyl, 96
Barnes Hospital, St. Louis, 23-24
Barton, Walter, 79, 84, 121
Barry, Anne, 134

Behavior: environmental response, 84-87, 136-137
Behavior modification. See Conditioning
Belknap, Ivan, 78
Bloomberg, Sanford, 142
Bogan, Louise, 79, 109-110
Borisov, Vladimir, 8, 53
Brandt, Anthony, 80
Breggin, Peter, 82
Bronx Psychiatric Center, N. Y., 6, 9
Bukovsky, Vladimir, 195
Byrd, Max, 3

Callender, Herbert, 61
Campbell, Coyne, 176
Chekhov, Anton, 53-54
China, People's Republic of: brainwashing centers, 8
Chu, Franklin, 77
Civil liberties, 4, 6, 64, 80, 83, 168-169
Clark, David, 81
Cohen, Richard, 176
Commitment proceedings, 5-6, 69-70
Community protection, 4, 5, 6
Conditioning, 14, 78; operant, 88-90; token economy, 78
Cornell, Julian, 56
Cotter, Lloyd M., 78, 88
Criminally dangerous persons, 6
Crisis treatment, need for, 67

BLUE JOLTS

Davenport, Eloise, 167, 211
Daymoon, Jackie, 83
Decision making, 86-87, 135, 140-141, 178-179
Dees, Walter, 176
Delusions: treatment, 125-126
Denner, Bruce, 77
Dependency, 4-5, 47, 50, 82-83, 135, 140-141, 167, 223-226
Depression, 142, 144, 204, 205; drug treatment, 110-111; postnatal, 180, 184; suicidal, 64-68
Diagnosis, 168; misdiagnosis, 45, 211-216; rights and responsibilities, 71-73
Disassociation, 7
Disorientation, 7-8
Dix Hill State Hospital, N.C., 101-103
Dobrovolsky, Aleksei, 195
Donaldson case, 168
Downs, Carol, 19, 20, 21
Drug addiction: treatment for, 71-73, 117-120
Drug therapy, 79, 97, 110-111
Drugs, 26, 39, 41, 69, 79-80; patient control, 107-108; punishment, 92-93, 95-96

Eagleton, Thomas F., 204
East Louisiana Mental Hospital, 177
Eberhart, Richard, 48
Edelson, Marshall, 83
Elderly, 5, 83
Electric shock treatment, xv, 47, 78-79, 110, 168, 211, 212-213; as anesthetic, 131, 132; as coercion, 88-89; as punishment, 81, 98-100
Elgin State Hospital, Ill., 38
Emotions: expressing, 148-149; situational, 84-87; suppressed, 150-151
England: mental hospitals, 1, 8, 104-108, 121-122, 185-190, 200-203

Family: adjusting to release of member, 223-226; conflicts, 16-22, 158-159; forced hospitalization of member, 10-26, 51; therapy, 19, 30-37, 158-161; vulnerability, 27-29, 178
Ferleger, David, 80
Fitzgerald, Zelda, 165
Food, as reinforcement, 78, 90
France: mental hospitals, 71-73
Freeman, Walter, 176
Friedberg, John, 78
Frost, Robert, 57
Fry, Jane, 83, 134

Ginsberg, Allen, 3, 25, 123, 218, 219
Glass, George S., 167, 209
Goffman, Erving, 7, 80
Gould, Miriam, 176
Gralnick, Alexander, 77
Grigorenki, Petr, 91
Grimes, Maurice, 7
Group dynamics, 82
Guardianship, 4, 5, 8

Haley, Jay, 78
Haloperidol, 92, 93, 96
Harassment therapy, 82, 127-129
Hemingway, Ernest, 5, 39-42, 44
Hemingway, Mary, 39-42
Hess, Rudolf, 56
Hoffman, Oscar, 177
Hospitalization: rationale, 4, 6-7; reinforcement of illness, 7, 27, 48, 82, 140-141, 167; right to, 64-68; stigma, 143, 167-168, 205, 207-210, 217-222
Hydrotherapy, 104-106, 109

Ibsen, Henrik, 3
Incest, 38
Individuality vs. social conformity, 38, 48-50, 72

Insanity vs. sanity, 3, 43, 44, 47-48, 49, 71-73, 168, 218-222
Institutionalization, 82-83, 140-141, 167, 223-226
Insulin-shock treatments, 45, 101-103, 211, 213
Isolation, 3, 27, 45, 46, 167, 220; as punishment, 81, 104

Johnson, Donald, 167, 200
Judicial review, 4, 56-57, 69-70

Kavka, Jerome, 56-60
Killian, Lewis, 83, 142
Krim, Herbert J., 44
Krim, Seymour, 167
Kruger, Judith, 166

Labeling, 6, 27, 45, 63, 143, 209-210
Larson, Willard, 4
Laws, Bolitha, 57
Leifer, Ronald, 81
Lennard, Henry, 79
Lexington, Ky.: Federal drug treatment center, 117-120
Limmer, Ruth, 109-111
Lobotomy, 82; prefrontal, 44; transorbital, 130-133
Long, Earl, 4, 25-26
Lord, Vernon, 39-42
Lorenz, Sarah, 83
Lowry, Malcolm, 168
Luxemburg, Rosa, 168

McCabe, Jack, 167, 223-226
McGowan, Edwin C., 177
Magruder, L. F., 177
Mandeville State Hospital, La., 25
Marks, Jan, 81, 117
Martin, John, 166
Martindale, Don, 6
Martindale, Edith, 6
Mayo Clinic, Minn., 39-42
Medication, 79-80; refusal, 80

Medvedev, Zhores, 91
Mental health system, 4, 64, 166
Mental hospitals: bureaucratic mismanagement, 64-68, 81, 121-122; custodial role, 4, 77; escapes, 166, 176-177; number of patients, 1; as prisons, 7, 8, 53-55, 72; release rate, 165, 166; use for political repression, see Political dissidents; See also Admissions; Mental patients; Release; Staff
Mental patients: civil liberties, 4, 6, 64, 80, 83, 168-169; coercion, 8-9, 88-90, 178; control of, 78, 80, 81, 98-100, 104-108; impersonal treatment of, 45, 82, 87, 103, 131-133, 138-139; interaction, 149-152; labeling of, 47, 50, 82; personal control, need for, 85-87; release rights, 24, 64, 205-206; research objects, 4, 16-22, 30-37, 159; responsibility and, 4-5, 136-137; self-perceptions, 86, 143; vulnerability, 3-4, 17, 82, 178-179
Mercier, Charles, 81
Milieu therapy, 3-37, 83, 134, 135, 137, 142-157; family interactions, 158-161
Miller, Kent, 4
Minorities, treatment of, 3, 5-6, 8, 61-63, 131-132
Murray, Jacquelyn, 166, 178

Napa State Hospital, Calif., 138-139
Nazis: use of mental hospitals, 8
Neary, John, 167
Neuroleptics, 93, 97
Neurological Institute, N. Y., 109-111
Neurotics, 82
New York Psychiatric Institute, 123-124

Occupational therapy (OT), 47, 123, 154, 202
Olson, Charles, 57
Overholser, Winfred, 56-57

Padded rooms, 104-105
Paraldehyde, 107
Patient confidentiality, 66
Patient culture, 84
Patient government, 83, 134-135, 148, 150
Perrucci, Robert, 83, 167, 191
Petrov, Vladimir, 91
Plath, Sylvia, xv
Plyushch, Leonid, 78, 91
Police: hospital admissions, 51-52, 65-66
Political dissidents, 8, 53-63, 78, 195-199; treatment, 91-97
Pound, Ezra, 8, 56-60
Price, Richard, 77
Psychiatrists, 6, 49; "authority", 27-29, 48, 57, 62-63, 71-72, *See also* Release interviews; lack of concurrence, 170-175; perception of patients, 4-5, 49, 62, 87
Psychoanalysis, 82
Psychosurgery, 81, 82, 130-133
Psychotherapy, 69, 82, 96
Punishment, 80-82; drugs, 92-93, 95-96; harassment, 127; shock treatment as, 98-100

Rage Reduction Therapy, 127
Recreation therapy, 82
Reddaway, Peter, 53, 91
Rees, T. P., 165
Reinforcement: negative, 89-90; positive, 78, 89, 90
Release, 20-21, 49, 165-226; adjusting to, 157, 223-226; patient's rights to, 24, 64, 205-206; police admissions, 52; policy, 166; uncertainty, effect of, 205; withholding, 178

Release interview, 166-167, 180-190; arbitrariness, 185-190; political dissidents, 196-199
Research, 4, 16-22, 30-37, 159
Rock, Ronald, 166
Rockland State Hospital, N. Y., 44
Roethke, Theodore, 109
Rogers, William, 57
Rokeach, Milton, 82, 125
Role perceptions, 82; behavior and, 86-87; maintenance, 99, 148; reversals, 209-210

Sadism, 127, 130-133
Saint Elizabeths Hospital, Wash., D. C., 56
Sanity. *See* Insanity
Scheff, Thomas, 7
Schimel, John, 7
Schizophrenic patients, 84-87, 130-133; chronic undifferentiated type, 138-139; hebephrenic, 140; treatment, 88-90
Sexuality, 114-115
Sheeley, William, 4
Shell-shock, 168
Shepherd and Enoch Pratt Hospital, Md., 136-137
Shimanov, Gennady, M., 167, 195-199
Shock therapy, 99; *See also* Electric shock treatment; Insulin-shock treatment
Siebert, Al, 6, 8, 69
Skeist, Robbie, 81
Smith, Charles, 165
Smith, Logan Pearsall, 101
Social therapy, 123-124
Social workers: commitment petition, 38
Sodium amytl, 107
Solomon, Carl, 82, 123
Spine, curvature of, 212-216
Staff: deceptions by, 8-9, 69-70, 178-179; hierarchy, 146; *See also* Attendants; Psychiatrists

Staff-patient relations, 78-83, 87, 127-129, 138-139, 142-156, 209-211

Stannard, D. L., 82, 127

Stern, Edith, 4

Stone, Alma, 80

Suicide: electric shock and, 79

Suicidal patients, 5, 27-29, 39-42, 46-47, 64-68, 205; release interview, 186-188

Sulfur injections, 92-93, 95-96

Supreme Court, 168

Szasz, Thomas, 7, 9, 167

Tarsis, Valery, 8, 53-55, 91

Therapeutic community. *See* Milieu therapy

Therapy, 109, 152; deception, 82, 125-126; family, 19, 30-37, 158-161; nondirective, 82; right to consent or refuse, 83; *See also* specific type of therapy

Thorazine, 69, 80

Torrey, E. Fuller, 78

Treatment, 77-161, *See also* Therapy

Trotter, Sharland, 77

Union of Soviet Socialist Republics: mental hospitals, 8, 53-55, 91-97, 195-199

United States: mental hospitals, 1, 8

Vail, David, 83, 140

Veterans Administration Hospitals, 134-135

Vietnam: mental hospitals, 88-90

Viscott, David, 17-22

Vocational therapy, 82

Wagner, Robert, 61

Walkenstein, Eileen, 82

Walker, Herbert, 78

Walter Reed Army Hospital, Wash., D. C., 84-87

Warr, Paul, 79, 167

Weitz, William, 77-78

Wells, Anna Mary, 166, 204

West, R. Frederick, 101-102

Williams, Tennessee, 4, 23-24

Wilson, Edmund, 109

Wilson, Tony, 170-175

Women: electroshock treatment, 88, 90

Work-release program, 88-90

Ypsilanti State Hospital, Mich., 125

Composed in Times Roman by New Republic Books.
Printed and bound by R.R. Donnelley, Crawfordsville, Indiana.
Designed by Gerard Valerio.